REVISE EDEXCEL GCSE
English
Language and Literature

REVISION WORKBOOK

Higher

Authors: Janet Beauman, David Grant, Alan Pearce,

Racheal Smith and Pam Taylor

- -

A note from the publisher

In order to ensure that this resource offers high-quality support for the associated Edexcel qualification, it has been through a review process by the awarding body to confirm that it fully covers the teaching and learning content of the specification or part of a specification at which it is aimed, and demonstrates an appropriate balance between the development of subject skills, knowledge and understanding, in addition to preparation for assessment.

While the publishers have made every attempt to ensure that advice on the qualification and its assessment is accurate, the official specification and associated assessment guidance materials are the only authoritative source of information and should always be referred to for definitive guidance.

Edexcel examiners have not contributed to any sections in this resource relevant to examination papers for which they have responsibility.

No material from an endorsed resource will be used verbatim in any assessment set by Edexcel.

Endorsement of a resource does not mean that the resource is required to achieve this Edexcel qualification, nor does it mean that it is the only suitable material available to support the qualification, and any resource lists produced by the awarding body shall include this and other appropriate resources.

For the full range of Pearson revision titles across GCSE, BTEC and AS Level visit:
www.pearsonschools.co.uk/revise

ALWAYS LEARNING

PEARSON

Contents

| Introduction | 4 |

English Language Unit 2

Section A: Reading

Lesson 1 Identifying language features and effects	6
ResultsPlus Build better answers	12
Lesson 2 Connecting language to presentation of characters and relationships	14
ResultsPlus Build better answers	20
Lesson 3 Connecting language to presentation of settings	22
ResultsPlus Build better answers	28
Lesson 4 Connecting language to presentation of ideas, themes and events	30
ResultsPlus Build better answers	36

Section B: Writing

Lesson 5 Starting the writing process	38
ResultsPlus Build better answers	44
Lesson 6 Developing and sustaining an idea	46
ResultsPlus Build better answers	52
Lesson 7 Effective word and sentence choices	54
ResultsPlus Build better answers	60
Lesson 8 Crafting and editing	62
ResultsPlus Build better answers	68

English Literature Unit 1

Section A: Literary Heritage

Lesson 1 Responding to characters | 70

ResultsPlus Build better answers | 76

Lesson 2 Responding to the writer's use of language | 78

ResultsPlus Build better answers | 84

Lesson 3 Exploring characters, relationships, events, ideas, themes and settings | 86

ResultsPlus Build better answers | 92

Section B: Different Cultures and Traditions

Lesson 4 Responding to an essay question | 94

ResultsPlus Build better answers | 100

Lesson 5 Responding to the context of the text | 102

ResultsPlus Build better answers | 108

Lesson 6 Spelling, punctuation and grammar | 110

ResultsPlus Build better answers | 120

English Literature Unit 2

Section A: Unseen Poetry

Lesson 1 Writing about an unseen poem | 122

ResultsPlus Build better answers | 128

Section B: Anthology Poems

Lesson 2 Commenting on one anthology poem | 130

ResultsPlus Build better answers | 136

Lesson 3 Comparing two poems | 138

ResultsPlus Build better answers | 144

This Workbook is designed to help you focus your revision and provide support as you prepare for your Edexcel GCSE English Language and Literature Higher Tier examinations.

Some students think that there is no need to revise for English examinations. This is simply not true! By making yourself familiar with the type of questions being asked, you will increase your chances of performing to your full potential in the examination.

How to improve your revision technique

1 The first thing to do is to make use of your teacher, as they are a very valuable resource! Listen carefully to all the revision guidance and tips your teacher gives you in lesson time. If there is something you are unsure about, remember to ask. Your teacher may hold extra revision classes at lunchtime in the run-up to the examinations. If so, make sure you take advantage of this opportunity.

2 Check that you are familiar with what the examination papers look like, how many marks are awarded to each question and how much time you will have in each examination. There is guidance on this provided opposite.

3 The most effective way to revise is through active strategies. This means:
   • practising the skills you have acquired throughout the course
   • taking part in completing revision activities to consolidate your knowledge
   • comparing your answers with sample answers to see exactly where you can improve your performance. You can do this using this Workbook.

Using the Revise Edexcel GCSE English Language and Literature Higher Student Workbook

This Workbook has been written to help you to revise the skills and knowledge that you will have covered in your GCSE English Language and Literature course. You may work through the book with your teacher within lessons. However, the activities in the Workbook are also suitable for you to complete during your own independent revision time.

 It has been designed for you to revise actively. There is room for you to write answers to activities and practise the skills required by completing sample examination questions. You are encouraged to highlight and annotate examination questions and texts as you might do in the examination itself.

The book is divided into three parts to reflect the Unit 2 Language, the Unit 1 Literature and Unit 2 Literature examinations. The tops of the pages are colour-coded to make it clear which part you are in.

As a reminder, here is a summary of the requirements for each Unit you will be taking:

English Language Unit 2: The Writer's Voice		
Time allowed		**Text allowed?**
1h 45 mins	**Section A: Reading**	Yes (clean copy)
	Section B: Writing	

English Literature Unit 1: Understanding Prose		
Time allowed		**Text allowed?**
1h 45 mins	**Section A: Literary Heritage**	Yes (clean copy)
	Section B: Different Cultures	

English Literature Unit 2: Understanding Poetry		
Time allowed		**Text allowed?**
1h 45 mins	**Section A: Unseen Poem**	
	Section B: Anthology Poems	Yes (clean copy)

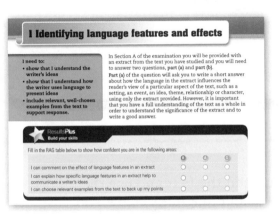

The following are some of the features that make this Workbook as user-friendly as possible:

- The lesson **introduction** will explain which part of the examination you will be revising for.

- **Learning objectives** at the start of each lesson explain what you will be aiming to achieve when answering this part of the examination.

- **ResultsPlus Build your skills** lists the skills you will be practising in the lesson and asks you to decide how confident you are with each of the skills listed – from red for 'not at all' to green for 'confident'. At the end of the lesson you will have the chance to review your confidence level again by filling in the same table. Your knowledge of the skills covered in the lesson should have improved.

- The **timer icon** gives a suggestion for how long you should spend on each activity. This is for guidance when working through the Workbook only - remember that this is not a suggestion for how long to spend on the examination question itself!

- **References** for extracts are included in this Workbook (e.g. chapter and page numbers) to allow you to look them up in your own copy and to re-inforce your knowledge of the text. These references are to the editions of the text which are listed as 'Prescribed texts' by Edexcel. Note that you will not be given a page reference for the extracts you are given in the examination question paper.

- **ResultsPlus Build better answers** give you an opportunity to read the mark schemes against which you will be assessed, and to match these to example student answers.

Finally, stay positive throughout your revision: think about what you can do, not what you can't. Good luck!

1 Identifying language features and effects

I need to:
- show that I understand the writer's ideas
- show that I understand how the writer uses language to present ideas
- include relevant, well-chosen examples from the text to support response.

In Section A of the examination you will be provided with an extract from the text you have studied and you will need to answer two questions, **part (a)** and **part (b)**.

Part (a) of the question will ask you to write a short answer about how the language in the extract influences the reader's view of a particular aspect of the text, such as a setting, an event, an idea, theme, relationship or character, using only the extract provided. However, it is important that you have a full understanding of the text as a whole in order to understand the significance of the extract and to write a good answer.

Activity 1

10 MINS

1 You need to be able to identify language features in the text and use the correct terms to describe them. Complete the spider diagrams below and opposite, adding as many language features as you can think of.

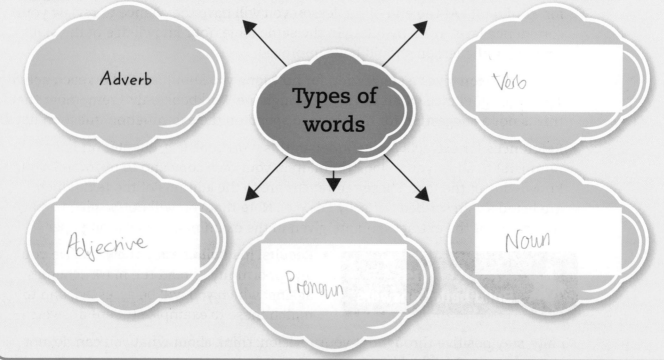

Adverb

Types of words

Verb

Adjective

Pronoun

Noun

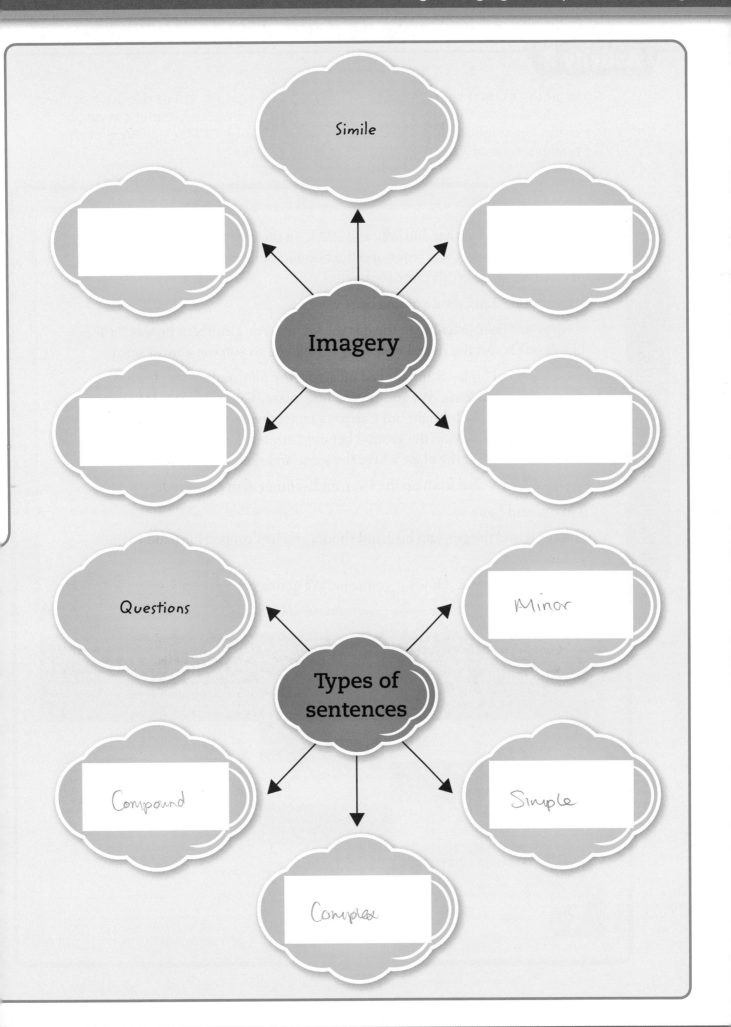

Simile

Imagery

Questions

Types of sentences

Minor

Compound

Simple

Complex

Activity 2

20 MINS

1 Read the extract below from the text you have studied. Fill in the table below to explain how the language in the extract influences the reader's view of either the relationship between George and Lennie (*Of Mice and Men*) **or** the reader's view of Tom Robinson (*To Kill a Mockingbird*).

Of Mice and Men, Section 6, pages 114–115

Lennie removed his hat dutifully and laid it on the ground in front of him. The shadow in the valley was bluer, and the evening came fast. On the wind the sound of crashing in the brush came to them.

Lennie said, 'Tell how it's gonna be.'

George had been listening to the distant sounds. For a moment he was business-like. 'Look acrost the river, Lennie, an' I'll tell you so you can almost see it.'

Lennie turned his head and looked off across the pool and up the darkening slopes of the Gabilans. 'We gonna get a little place,' George began. He reached in his side pocket and brought out Carlson's Luger; he snapped off the safety, and the hand and gun lay on the ground behind Lennie's back. He looked at the back of Lennie's head, at the place where the spine and skull were joined.

A man's voice called from up the river, and another man answered.

'Go on,' said Lennie.

George raised the gun and his hand shook, and he dropped his hand to the ground again.

'Go on,' said Lennie. 'How's it gonna be. We gonna get a little place.'

	Example	Name of language feature	How this influences the reader's view of the relationship between George and Lennie
1		Adverb	
2	he was business-like		
3		Verb	
4	'Look acrost the river'		
5		Repetition	

'Tom, you're sworn to tell the whole truth. Will you tell it?'

Tom ran his hand nervously over his mouth.

'What happened after that?'

'Answer the question,' said Judge Taylor. One-third of his cigar had vanished.

'Mr Finch, I got down offa that chair an' turned around an' she sorta jumped on me.'

'Jumped on you? Violently?'

'No suh, she – she hugged me. She hugged me round the waist.'

This time Judge Taylor's gavel came down with a bang, and as it did the overhead lights went on in the courtroom. Darkness had not come, but the afternoon sun had left the windows. Judge Taylor quickly restored order.

'Then what did she do?'

The witness swallowed hard. 'She reached up an' kissed me 'side of th' face. She says she never kissed a grown man before an' she might as well kiss a nigger. She says what her papa do to her don't count. She says, "Kiss me back, nigger." I say Miss Mayella lemme outa here an' tried to run but she got her back to the door an' I'da had to push her. I didn't wanta harm her, Mr Finch, an' I say lemme pass, but just when I say it Mr Ewell yonder hollered through th' window.'

'What did he say?'

Tom Robinson swallowed again, and his eyes widened. 'Somethin' not fittin' to say – not fittin' for these folks'n chillun to hear – '

	Example	Name of language feature	How this influences the reader's view of Tom Robinson
1	'She – she hugged me. She hugged me round the waist.'		
2		Colloquial language	
3		Verbs	
4		Long sentences	
5	'not fittin' for these folks'n chillun to hear'		

Activity 3

20 MINS

1 Read the extracts from students' responses below. The students are exploring how the language in the extract on pages 8–9 influences the reader's view of **either** the relationship between George and Lennie (*Of Mice and Men*) **or** the reader's view of Tom (*To Kill a Mockingbird*). Look at the feedback for each response and try to improve each one using the suggestions given.

Of Mice and Men

Response A

The writer used the adjective 'business-like' to show George's behaviour.

Feedback

The student has given an example from the text, but has not included any explanation of what this example shows or the effect on the reader. It is not clear whether the student understands the writer's ideas or not.

Explain what this adjective shows and how it influences the reader's view of the relationship between Lennie and George.

_____

_____

_____

_____

Response B

John Steinbeck uses language to show that George and Lennie are very close. The extract shows Lennie's dependency on George.

Feedback

The student makes a good point, but it lacks support.

Continue the paragraph to include some evidence from the text.

_____

_____

_____

_____

To Kill a Mockingbird

Response A

The writer uses language to show that Tom is nervous and not used to being in a formal situation such as a courtroom.

Feedback

The student makes a good point, but it lacks support.

Continue the paragraph to include some evidence from the extract.

_____

_____

_____

_____

Response B

Harper Lee uses colloquial speech in this extract which is an effective technique to show the character of Tom.

Feedback

This point needs to be developed and explained fully — the student has not explained what the colloquial speech reveals about Tom.

Develop the explanation so that it refers closely to the text and comments on the effect of the language on the reader.

_____

_____

_____

_____

_____

10 MINS

Look back at the extract on pages 8–9.

1   Read the extracts below from student answers explaining how the language in the extract influences our view of Lennie and George's relationship **or** our view of Tom Robinson. Then match the sample answer to the feedback which you think describes it.

Of Mice and Men

Student 1

In this extract we see how Lennie trusts and depends on George, and how George cares for him and reassures him, even though he is about to kill him. The author uses the adverb 'dutifully' in the first line to show how Lennie does as George tells him unquestioningly. George uses a lot of commands and this shows that he has more power in the relationship. For example, he says 'Look across the river, Lennie...' and Lennie immediately turns his head.

Student 2

George reassures Lennie and makes him feel more confident by repeating some of what he says, for example he repeats 'For the rabbits' after Lennie. This shows that he takes care of Lennie. Lennie looks to George like a parent telling him a bedtime story when he is describing the way things are going to be. The language shows that Lennie does as George tells him, like a child. We also see that George doesn't want to kill Lennie and is trying to hide his emotion.

Feedback A

The candidate shows a thorough exploration of how Steinbeck uses techniques to create effect - all points are linked to the effect on the reader. There is thorough understanding of how techniques contribute to the relationship between George and Lennie and the connection is consistently made between techniques and their relationship. The techniques are identified correctly. All points have textual reference to support the response.

Feedback B

The candidate does identify what the relationship between George and Lennie is like but does not go into much detail on how techniques are used to show this. The understanding of how techniques contribute to presentation of the relationship appears sound and some very good points are made, but there are not a lot of examples from the text to support the points and the features are not identified.

Student 1

The writer uses language to show that Tom is remembering an incident and telling what happened, so he speaks using lots of 'I said, she said' language and verbs to show what happened such as 'done', 'reachin'', 'grabbed' and 'turned'. Tom uses colloquial language like 'Naw, suh' and 'I done' which tells the reader that he is not very educated. Tom hesitates a lot and repeats himself ('She – she hugged me. She hugged me round the waist').

Student 2

In this extract, Tom is very nervous and frightened. The words 'swallowed hard' and 'his eyes widened' emphasise his fear. Adverbs such as 'nervously' are also used to show the reader how frightened he is. Tom also hesitates and repeats words, showing that he is scared to tell the truth 'she – she hugged me'.

Feedback A

The candidate shows a thorough exploration of how the author uses techniques to build up the reader's view of Tom. The connection is consistently made between techniques and the depiction of his character. The techniques are identified correctly. All points have textual reference to support the response.

Feedback B

In the first point, the candidate has correctly identified language techniques, but the examples and explanation are not relevant to the question. The second point identifies language techniques and explained how these influence the reader, but the point could be developed further. In the third point, the candidate identifies language techniques but not their effect.

ResultsPlus
Build your skills

Fill in the RAG table below to see how your confidence has improved in the following areas:

	R	A	G
I can comment on the effect of language features in an extract	○	○	○
I can explain how specific language features in an extract help to communicate a writer's ideas	○	○	○
I can choose relevant examples from the text to back up my points	○	○	○

2 Connecting language to presentation of characters and relationships

I need to:
- show that I understand the writer's ideas about characters and relationships
- show that I understand how the writer uses language to present characters and relationships
- include relevant, well-chosen examples from the text to back up my points.

You may have to answer a question about characters and relationships in **part (a)** or **part (b)** of the examination. In this lesson you will look at how the writer has used language to influence our view of characters and their relationships. It is important that you have a good knowledge of the key characters within the text you have studied in order to be able to pinpoint examples of language in an extract that show your understanding.

ResultsPlus
Build your skills

Fill in the RAG table below to show how confident you are in the following areas:

	R	A	G
I can explain what the writer has shown about a character or relationship	○	○	○
I can explain why the writer has used specific language features to influence the reader's view of a character or relationship	○	○	○
I can choose good examples from the text to back up my points	○	○	○

Activity 1

10 MINS

1   Choose one of the main characters in the text you have studied and complete the tables below to summarise three character traits, the places in the text where these are shown, and the language the writer uses to influence our view of the characters. Examples from each text are given below to help you.

The reader's view of the character	Section of the text	Language used in the extract which influences our view of the character
Lennie has conflicting feelings	Start of Section 5, pages 92–93, in the hay barn	'put out his huge hand and stroked it' 'said softly to the puppy' 'Suddenly his anger rose' 'He turned his back on it' 'He rocked himself back and forth in his sorrow'
Scout is observant	Chapter 28, pages 267–268, coming home from the Halloween pageant	'Our company shuffled and dragged his feet' 'Soft swish of cotton on cotton, wheek, wheek, with every step' 'I felt the sand go cold under my feet' 'Jem pressed my head'

Character: _____

	The reader's view of the character	Section of the text	Language used in the extract which influences our view of the character

2 Now fill in the table below in the same way, to think about how the reader's view of a relationship is influenced by the language in different sections of the text.

Relationship: _____

	The reader's view of the relationship	Section of the text	Language used in the extract which influences our view of the relationship

Activity 2

Read the short extract below which is relevant to the text you have studied, and then answer the questions which follow to help you think about the language used to present character. Remember that you won't get questions like this on an extract in the exam.

Of Mice and Men, Section 5, pages 94–95

> She said, 'What you got there, sonny boy?'
>
> Lennie glared at her. 'George says I ain't to have nothing to do with you – talk to you or nothing.'
>
> She laughed. 'George giving you orders about everything?'
>
> Lennie looked down at the hay. 'Says I can't tend no rabbits if I talk to you or anything.'
>
> She said quietly, 'He's scared Curley'll get mad. Well, Curley got his arm in a sling – an' if Curley gets tough, you can break his other han'. You didn't put nothing over on me about gettin' it caught in no machine.'
>
> But Lennie was not to be drawn. 'No, sir. I ain't gonna talk to you or nothing.'
>
> She knelt in the hay beside him. 'Listen,' she said. 'All the guys got a horseshoe tenement goin' on. It's on'y about four o'clock. None of them guys is goin' to leave that tenement. Why can't I talk to you? I never get to talk to nobody. I get awful lonely.'
>
> Lennie said, 'Well I ain't supposed to talk to you or nothing.'
>
> 'I get lonely,' she said. 'You can talk to people, but I can't talk to nobody but Curley. Else he gets mad. How'd you like not to talk to anybody?'

a   What do we learn about Curley's wife when she says 'He's scared Curley'll get mad … gettin' it caught in no machine'?

_____

_____

b   Find some examples of the use of questions by Curley's wife. What do these questions tell us about her character?

_____

_____

c   What is the effect of the repetition 'I get awful lonely…I get lonely'?

_____

_____

To Kill a Mockingbird, Chapter 28, pages 267–268

Jem knew as well as I that it was difficult to walk fast without stumping a toe, tripping on stones, and other inconveniences, and I was barefooted. Maybe it was the wind rustling the trees. But there wasn't any wind and there weren't any trees except the big oak.

Our company shuffled and dragged his feet, as if wearing heavy shoes. Whoever it was wore thick cotton pants; what I thought were trees rustling was the soft swish of cotton on cotton, wheek, wheek, with every step.

I felt the sand go cold under my feet and I knew we were near the big oak. Jem pressed my head. We stopped and listened.

Shuffle-foot had not stopped with us this time. His trousers swished softly and steadily. Then they stopped. He was running, running towards us with no child's steps.

'Run, Scout! Run! Run!' Jem screamed.

a What words or phrases in the extract show us that Scout is observant and thinks things through carefully?

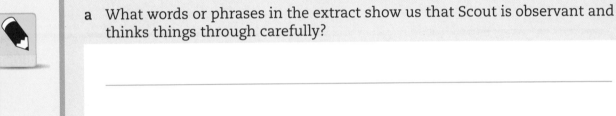

b What words or phrases in the extract does Scout use to refer to the person following them? What do these tell us about her character?

c What do the references to Jem tell us about Scout's relationship with him?

Activity 3

In **part (b)** of your examination, you will need to think about how the writer presents a similar character, relationship, idea, theme or setting in one other part of the text. You will need to choose your own extract from the text in order to do this.

1   In this lesson you have focused on how language is used to present a character or relationship. Choose another extract from the text you have studied in which the writer presents an aspect of the relationship between two main characters.

2   Look at the extract carefully and pick out five examples of language which the writer has used to tell the reader something about their relationship.

3   Now write five questions like those on pages 16–17 about the language you have picked out to help other students revise this extract. Use the form below but leave the 'Answer' sections blank for now. Make sure you can answer the questions yourself though!

Chosen extract: _____

Significance of this extract: _____

_____

Language example: _____

Question:

_____

Answer:

_____

_____

_____

Language example: _____

Question:

_____

Answer:

_____

_____

Language example: _____

Question:

_____

Answer:

_____

_____

_____

Language example: _____

Question:

_____

Answer:

_____

_____

_____

Language example: _____

Question:

_____

Answer:

_____

_____

_____

4   When you have prepared your questions, swap books with a partner who has chosen
    a different extract and answer each other's questions.

10 MINS

1 Look at the student response to a part (b) sample examination question relevant to the text you have studied, below or opposite. Decide which band the response falls into and explain your choice.

Band	Description
3	• Thorough understanding of the text • Thorough understanding of the writer's ideas • Thorough understanding of how the writer uses language • Sustained reference to the extract to support response.
4	• Assured understanding of the text • Assured understanding of the writer's ideas • Assured understanding of how the writer uses language • Pertinent reference to the text to support response.
5	• Perceptive understanding of the text • Perceptive understanding of the writer's ideas • Perceptive understanding of how the writer uses language • Discriminating reference to the extract to support response.

Of Mice and Men

Explore how the writer presents the relationship between George and Lennie in **one other** part of the novel.   (24 marks)

In the first section of the book, Steinbeck shows that George and Lennie are very close and that George looks after Lennie like a parent would. Lennie is like a child trying to emotionally blackmail George by saying 'If you don't want me, you only jus' got to say so, and I'll go off in those hills right there'. George uses an affirmative statement to make it directly clear to Lennie that he doesn't want him to do that, as he says 'I want you to stay with me, Lennie'.

George is concerned for Lennie and uses the comparison of Lennie to a 'coyote' to show that he is like an animal and wouldn't be able to look after himself as he says 'somebody'd shoot you'. Steinbeck uses the adverb 'craftily' to show that Lennie knows he can manipulate George at some points and that he is aware that George wants to look after him.

Explore how the character of Scout is presented in **one other** part of the novel.

(24 marks)

Scout is presented as thoughtful and learning a lot during the book. She is presented as a character who is keen to learn and after her first day at school in Chapter 3 she learns not to judge someone because of what they say to you. Scout has trouble getting along with Miss Caroline and makes a judgement about her because she thinks Atticus has taught her to read in the wrong way. Scout shows her loyalty to her father by asking Atticus if she can no longer attend school and asking him if he could 'teach me like Granddaddy taught you'n' Uncle Jack'. Atticus tells her 'You never really understand a person until you consider things from his point of view ... until you climb into his skin and walk around in it.' This makes Scout reconsider her opinion of Miss Caroline which shows she is intelligent and reflective. She also shows she is clever by trying to get out of school by using 'precedent' of Burris Ewell, who 'just goes to school the first day' to get his name on the roll.

I think the student would achieve a Band _____ because _____

_____

_____

_____

Build your skills

Fill in the RAG table below to see how your confidence has improved in the following areas:

	R	A	G
I can explain what the writer has shown about a character or relationship	○	○	○
I can explain why the writer has used specific language features to influence the reader's view of a character or relationship	○	○	○
I can choose good examples from the text to back up my points	○	○	○

3 Connecting language to presentation of settings

I need to:

- show that I understand the writer's ideas about settings
- show that I understand how the writer uses language to present settings
- include relevant, well-chosen examples from the text to back up my points.

In the examination, you may be asked to comment on how the writer uses language to present a particular place in either **part (a)** or **part (b)**. It is important to understand the different settings of the text and their significance in order to comment effectively on how they are presented using the language in the extract.

ResultsPlus
Build your skills

Fill in the RAG table below to show how confident you are in the following areas:

	R	A	G
I can explain what the writer has shown about a setting	○	○	○
I can explain why the writer has used specific language features to influence the reader's view of a setting	○	○	○
I can choose good examples from the text to back up my points	○	○	○

Activity 1

10 MINS

1 Complete the spider diagram with the four most important settings in the text you have studied. Write **where** in the text they are presented and some examples of the language used to present each one.

Below is one example from *Of Mice and Men* and one example from *To Kill a Mockingbird* to start you off.

Setting:

The pool

Section in the text:

Section 1

Language used to present the setting:

The water is described as a place where animals come to find safety as there are trees personified with 'melted, white, recumbent limbs' that arch over the pool in a protective gesture.

Setting:

Boo Radley's house

Section in the text:

Chapter 6

Language used to present the setting:

The back of the Radley house is described as 'less inviting' than the front. This shows irony in that the front is not inviting at all, so to be 'less inviting' would be difficult.

Setting:

_____

Section in the text:

_____

Language used to present the setting:

_____

_____

Setting:

_____

Section in the text:

_____

Language used to present the setting:

_____

Language used to
present settings

Setting:

_____

Section in the text:

_____

Language used to present the setting:

_____

_____

Setting:

_____

Section in the text:

_____

Language used to present the setting:

_____

_____

Activity 2

When you answer part (a) of the examination question, you will need to include examples from a given extract in your answer. The following activity will help you to practise doing this.

1 Read the sample examination question and extract from the text you have studied. Make notes around the text on how the highlighted language influences your view of the setting. Identify any other language that may help you to answer the question.

Of Mice and Men, Section 1, page 1

> Explore how the language in this extract influences your view of the setting.
> (24 marks)

A few miles south of Soledad, the Salinas River drops in close to the hillside bank and runs deep and green. The water is warm too, for it has slipped twinkling over the yellow sands in the sunlight before reaching the narrow pool. On one side of the river the golden foothill slopes curve up to the strong and rocky Gablian mountains, but on the valley side the water is lined with trees – willows fresh and green with every spring, carrying in their lower leaf junctures the debris of the winter's flooding; and sycamores with mottled, white, recumbent limbs and branches that arch over the pool. On the sandy bank under the trees the leaves lie deep and so crisp that a lizard makes a great skittering if he runs among them. Rabbits come out of the brush to sit on the sand in the evening, and the damp flats are covered with the night tracks of 'coons, and with the spread pads of dogs from the ranches, and with the split-wedge tracks of deer that come to drink in the dark.

Explore how the language in this extract influences your view of the Ewells' home.   (16 marks)

To Kill a Mockingbird, Chapter 17, pages 176 –177

Maycomb Ewells lived behind the town garbage dump in what was once a Negro cabin. The cabin's plank walls were supplemented with sheets of corrugated iron, its roof shingled with tin cans hammered flat, so only its general shape suggested its original design: square, with four tiny rooms opening on to a shotgun hall, the cabin rested uneasily upon four irregular lumps of limestone. Its windows were merely open spaces in the walls, which in the summertime were covered with greasy strips of cheesecloth to keep out the varmints that feasted on Maycomb's refuse.

The varmints had a lean time of it, for the Ewells gave the dump a thorough gleaning every day, and the fruits of their industry (those that were not eaten) made the plot of ground around the cabin look like the playhouse of an insane child: what passed for a fence was bits of tree-limbs, broomsticks and tool shafts, all tipped with rusty hammer-heads, snaggle-toothed rake heads, shovels, axes and grubbing hoes, held on with pieces of barbed wire.

2 Write one paragraph below in response to the sample examination question, including some of the highlighted examples in the text and any others you think are relevant.

Activity 3

25 MINS

When you answer part (b) of the examination question, you will need to choose an extract of your own to focus on. This activity will help you to practise doing that.

1   Read the sample examination question below:

> Explore how the writer presents a setting in **one other** part of the text.
>
> Use examples of the language the writer uses to support your ideas.
>
> (24 marks)

Remember, a setting can be outside or indoors. For example, it can be someone's private house, inside a public building, a street, a field or any part of a landscape.

2   Find three possible **short** extracts from the text you have studied which would be suitable to answer the sample examination question. List the setting that is described in each extract below, along with a chapter or section reference for each one. You might want to look back at your answers to Activity 1 to help you.

Extract 1 _____

Extract 2 _____

Extract 3 _____

3   Choose one of the above extracts in which language is used to present a setting and read it carefully. Pick out some examples of the writer's language and make some notes on how this influences the reader's view of the setting.

_____

_____

_____

_____

_____

_____

_____

_____

4 Write two or three paragraphs of your answer to the sample examination question, using the examples you have identified in your notes. Remember, you must just refer to your chosen short extract, not the rest of the text!

10 MINS

1 Remind yourself of the mark scheme on page 20. Then look at the sample student answers to the sample examination question from page 26, which appear below.

Which band do you think the student would get? Think about the following:

- How well have the students understood the writer's use of language?
- Did they go beyond the obvious in explaining the effect of the language?
- How relevant are the examples they have given?

Of Mice and Men

The description of the bunk house begins 'was a long rectangular building' showing how it is simplistic but is also creates a general setting for the writer to expand on. Inside 'the walls were whitewashed and floor unpainted'. The words 'whitewashed' and 'unpainted' show a basic clinical design that is uninviting and is similar to a prison. 'In 3 walls were small square windows' reinforces this idea as the windows are 'small' and will not allow room to escape or to let light in. 'A solid wooden door' again seems to be prison-like as the door is 'solid' and unlikely to be broken.

'5 of them were made up while the other 3 showed their burlap' describes the bunks, firstly the fact that 3 are empty implies a deserted area. They are also unused as they show their mattresses. There was nailed-on apple boxes over each bunk to provide space for personal belongings. The apple box is a fragile container full of the little that these men own. It could be seen as a metaphor for the dream these men have. They are fragile, but they hold all their own. Shelves are 'loaded with little articles, soap, razors and western magazines'. Almost all of these items are purely functional and masculine. 'Western magazines that ranch men love to read and scoff at and secretly believe' again shows the fragile dreams and hope that the men here have.

Student A

Lee describes the county court-house in chapter 16 of the novel. She describes it as being like Arlington which makes us think about the respect people have for the court-house. The 'concrete pillars supporting its south roof were too heavy for their burden'. The words 'heavy' and 'burden' show the seriousness of the court house and what happens there. The fact that the pillars are all that were left after 'the original court-house burned in 1865' suggests the court-house is powerful and cannot be destroyed. The court-house is described as presenting 'an unoffensive vista' which makes it sound like it is nice but not really nice. The architecture is described as 'clashing' which again reflects what happens inside the court house. The mixture of Greek and Victorian architecture make it seems as if the court-house is not sure what it is supposed to be which is contrary to what it does. The 'rusty unreliable instrument' in the clock tower gives the reader the impression that the clock doesn't work but that the local people are very set in their ways and don't want to change anything. Lee uses alliteration to describe the journey to the court-room past 'sundry sunless county cubby-holes' which makes it seem dark and secretive.

I would award the student a Band _____ because _____

_____

_____

Results Plus
Build your skills

Fill in the RAG table below to see how your confidence has improved in the following areas:

	R	A	G
I can explain what the writer has shown about a setting	○	○	○
I can explain why the writer has used specific language features to influence the reader's view of a setting	○	○	○
I can choose good examples from the text to back up my points	○	○	○

4 Connecting language to presentation of ideas, themes and events

I need to:

- show that I understand the writer's ideas and themes and the events of the texts
- show that I understand how the writer uses language to present ideas, themes and events
- include relevant, well-chosen examples to support my points.

Instead of a character, a relationship or a setting, you might be asked to explain how language is used to present a key idea, theme or event in an extract. This lesson will give you practice commenting on the effect of this language. Remember that in **part (a)**, you will be given an extract to comment on. In **part (b)** you will need to choose your own extract.

ResultsPlus
Build your skills

Fill in the RAG table below to show how confident you are in the following areas:

	R	A	G
I can explain what the writer has shown about a particular idea, theme or event	○	○	○
I can explain why the writer has used language to present key ideas, themes and events in the text	○	○	○
I can choose good examples from the text to back up my points	○	○	○

Activity 1

To build good answers, you need to have an excellent understanding of the whole text. You need to know what happens, and you also need to know about the text's key ideas: what the writer wants the reader to understand, think and feel.

10 MINS

1   Complete the spider diagram opposite, showing the key ideas and themes in the text you have studied, along with the language used to present these.

Idea, theme or event

Friendship

Section in the text:

Section 2 when George defends Lennie against Curley

Language used to present the idea, theme or event:

'Spose he don't want to talk?'
'We travel together,' said George coldly

Shows how George is determined to stand up for Lennie

Idea, theme or event

Race

Section in the text:

Chapter 12 where Calpurnia takes Scout and Jem to her church

Language used to present the idea, theme or event:

The warm bittersweet smell of clean Negro
'Why do you talk nigger-talk...?'

Shows how Calpurnia's world is different and strange to the children

---

Idea, theme or event:

_____

Section in the text:

_____

Language used to present the

Idea, theme or event: _____

_____

Idea, theme or event:

_____

Section in the text:

_____

Language used to present the

Idea, theme or event: _____

_____

Language used to present ideas, themes and events

Idea, theme or event:

_____

Section in the text:

_____

Language used to present the

Idea, theme or event: _____

_____

Idea, theme or event:

_____

Section in the text:

_____

Language used to present the

Idea, theme or event: _____

_____

Activity 2

15 MINS

1   Look at the extract from the text you have studied along with the sample part (a) examination question. Identify and then highlight four examples of language which will be relevant in answering the question.

Of Mice and Men, Section 5, page 93

> Explore how the language in the extract influences your view of Lennie's feelings.
>
> (16 marks)

He unburied the puppy and inspected it, and he stroked it from ears to tail. He went on sorrowfully, 'But he'll know. George always know. He'll say, "You done it. Don't try to put nothing over on me." An' he'll say, "Now jus' for that you don't get to tend no rabbits!"'

Suddenly his anger arose. 'God damn you,' he cried. 'Why do you got to get killed? You ain't so little as mice.' He picked up the pup and hurled it from him. He turned his back on it. He sat bent over his knees and he whispered, 'Now I won't get to tend the rabbits. Now he won't let me.' He rocked himself back and forth in his sorrow.

To Kill a Mockingbird, Chapter 10, pages 103–104

> Explore how the language in the extract influences your view of how the children's ideas about their father are changed.
>
> (16 marks)

Jem became vaguely articulate: ''d you see'd him, Scout? 'd you see him just standin' there?... 'n' all of a sudden he just relaxed all over, an' it looked like that gun was a part of him … an' he did it so quick, like … I hafta aim for ten minutes 'fore I can hit somethin'…'

Miss Maudie grinned wickedly. 'Well now, Miss Jean Louise,' she said, 'still think your father can't do anything? Still ashamed of him?'

'Nome,' I said meekly.

'Forgot to tell you the other day that besides playing the Jew's Harp, Atticus Finch was the deadest shot in Maycomb County in his time.'

'Dead shot…' echoed Jem.

'That's what I said, Jem Finch. Guess you'll change *your* tune now. The very idea, didn't you know his nickname was Ol' One-Shot when he was a boy? Why, down at the Landing when he was coming up, if he shot fifteen times and hit fourteen doves he'd complain about wasting ammunition.'

'He never said anything about that,' Jem muttered.

2 Now write at least two PEE points (point, evidence and explanation) to explore how these examples of language influence your view of Lennie's feelings (*Of Mice and Men*) or of how the children's ideas about their father are changed (*To Kill a Mockingbird*).

Activity 3

25 MINS

Below are two sample questions for Section A, part (b) of the examination.

1   Read the question for your chosen text and note down three possible extracts from your text you could focus on in your response.

Of Mice and Men

> In the extract Lennie's feelings are presented.
>
> Explore how Lennie's feelings are presented in **one other** part of the novel.
>
> Use examples of the language the writer uses to support your ideas.
>
> (24 marks)

To Kill a Mockingbird

> In the novel, the children's changing ideas are important.
>
> Explore how the children's ideas are changed in **one other** part of the novel.
>
> Use examples of the language the writer uses to support your ideas.
>
> (24 marks)

Extracts I could use to answer this question:

1. _____

2. _____

3. _____

2   Choose one of the extracts you identified above and find at least four language features that influence the reader's view of the idea or theme specified in the question.

_____

_____

_____

_____

_____

	Example of language	How this influences the reader's view of the theme or idea
1		
2		
3		
4		

3 Now write at least two paragraphs of a response to the sample part (b) question opposite, using the language features you have already identified. You might want to remind yourself of the mark scheme on page 36 of your workbook.

_____

_____

_____

_____

_____

_____

_____

_____

_____

_____

_____

Build better answers

10 MINS

1 Remind yourself of the mark scheme (below) and read through your response to the sample examination question in Activity 3.

Band	Description
3	• Thorough understanding of the text • Thorough understanding of the writer's ideas • Thorough understanding of how the writer uses language • Sustained reference to the extract to support response
4	• Assured understanding of the text • Assured understanding of the writer's ideas • Assured understanding of how the writer uses language • Pertinent reference to the extract to support response
5	• Perceptive understanding of the text • Perceptive understanding of the writer's ideas • Perceptive understanding of how the writer uses language • Discriminating reference to the extract to support response

2 Think about how you might improve your response. Ask yourself the following questions, adding notes around your writing in response:

- Have you made 'perceptive' points that go beyond the obvious?
- Have you commented on why the writer has used specific language?
- Have you included the best, most relevant examples from the text that you can find?

Write down three things you could do to make your response better.

_____

_____

_____

_____

_____

_____

3 Rewrite part of your response here, making improvements as necessary.

_____

_____

_____

_____

_____

_____

_____

_____

_____

_____

_____

_____

_____

_____

ResultsPlus
Build your skills

Fill in the RAG table below to see how your confidence has improved in the following areas:

	R	A	G
I can explain what the writer has shown about a particular idea, theme or event	○	○	○
I can explain why the writer has used language to present key ideas, themes and events in the text	○	○	○
I can choose good examples from the text to back up my points	○	○	○

I need to:
- learn the steps for beginning an examination response
- structure responses so that they are appropriate for audience, purpose and form
- create an effective opening sentence.

This lesson will show you a step-by-step process that will make it easier to get started when you tackle Section B of the English Language examination.

You should practise these steps as part of your preparation. You will:

- analyse the question so you know what you are aiming to do

- form a paragraph map

- come up with a powerful opening line that will appeal to your audience, suit the purpose and be appropriate for the form you are writing in.

In this lesson you will practise this process and learn how to plan your response effectively.

ResultsPlus
Build your skills

Fill in the RAG table below to show how confident you are in the following areas:

	R	A	G
I know how to analyse a question in order to understand what choices to make	○	○	○
I know how to organise ideas effectively and create a paragraph plan	○	○	○
I know how to use structure and vocabulary to write an engaging and compelling opening sentence	○	○	○

Activity 1

15 MINS

1 In your examination, you will be asked to write about a subject that you will be familiar with. Complete a mind map around this teenager. What subjects might she write about?

2 Look at the words in the box below. These are all words you might find in an examination question. Place each word into the correct column in the table according to whether it tells you about the **purpose** of your writing, the **audience** for your writing or the **form** in which you should write.

Purpose	Audience	Form

speech   teacher
inform   MP
review   explain
argue   local community
parents   letter
article   text for a leaflet
peers

To analyse the question properly, you need to make notes about some of the choices you will make – for example, the kind of language you would use to suit the audience. An example is given below:

Form: start with 'Dear Sir/Madam' or name. Use appropriate sign off

Explain points and give evidence. Be persuasive!

> Write a letter to the local council arguing for more sports clubs for young people in your area. (24 marks)

Adults I don't know: formal, don't use slang, serious and respectful tone

Need more, give specific suggestions

3 Now look at the examination question that appears below. Make your own notes around the question to record the key decisions you would make about the content and tone of your writing that are appropriate for the purpose, audience and form.

> Write an article for a teenage magazine in which you suggest fitness activities that you think young people would enjoy.
> (24 marks)

Activity 2

Look closely at the examination question below along with one student's plan for their writing.

10 MINS

1 Work to improve this plan. You should cross out, add to and reorganise the ideas.

Form: formal — address audience — you/we — use patterns of three to get tone right

Give an opinion: draw in examples — quite informative

> Write the text for a speech in which you comment on homework to the school council.   (24 marks)

Peers: maybe offer some light-hearted moments?! But formal setting

Ban it: not good

Paragraph 1: Shared idea of what homework is like
- boring
- irrelevant
- too easy/too hard

Paragraph 2: Why teachers like it
- make us suffer
- supposed to help us get organised
- very little reason

Paragraph 3: How it could be better
- big projects
- student choice
- mix of activities

Paragraph 4: No homework
- use time to volunteer
- work on practical stuff
- have fun

2 Write a paragraph explaining why your changes have made the plan more effective.

3 Write a list of five features which help to make an effective plan.

1

2

3

4

5

Activity 3

20 MINS

It is important to try and make the first sentence of your writing as engaging and compelling as possible so that your reader (in this case, the examiner) gets a positive first impression.

1 Complete the table below which contains a range of possible openings for a piece of writing in response to the examination question in Activity 2 on page 40. You should tick in the column if you think the opening has:

- used an effective choice of sentence structure
- used appropriate and sophisticated vocabulary
- selected a strong and engaging tone.

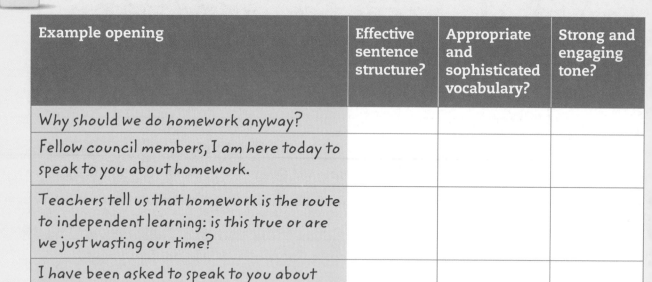

Example opening	Effective sentence structure?	Appropriate and sophisticated vocabulary?	Strong and engaging tone?
Why should we do homework anyway?			
Fellow council members, I am here today to speak to you about homework.			
Teachers tell us that homework is the route to independent learning: is this true or are we just wasting our time?			
I have been asked to speak to you about homework.			
I know it's really not that controversial to say but I really hate homework!			

2 Use what you have learned about successful openings to write an opening sentence for an answer to the following examination question:

> Write a letter to your headteacher arguing for a change in school uniform policy.
> (24 marks)

_____

_____

_____

To make sure you know where you are going in your writing, it is also a good idea to write the final sentence of your response. It is a good strategy to try to make it link to your opening sentence in terms of style, tone and content.

3 Write a closing sentence to match the opening sentence you have just written.

4 Explain the choices you have made regarding sentence structure, vocabulary choice and tone in your opening and closing sentences. What makes them effective and compelling?

5 Now it's time to write a complete plan for a response to an examination question. You have eight minutes to complete the whole process, which is roughly the amount of time you will have in the exam itself. Remember the four steps in the planning process:

1 Annotate the question with your ideas.

2 Write a plan.

3 Write an opening sentence.

4 Write a closing sentence.

> Write an article for a lifestyle magazine in which you discuss the benefits and drawbacks of modern technology. (24 marks)

To build a good answer you need to make your writing compelling. This means you need to evoke powerful thoughts or emotions in your reader and maintain a strong sense of 'voice' in your writing.

Look at the following two plans for the same examination question.

1 Which piece of writing do you think is the most compelling?

Plan 1   *Chatty, informal, references to other stuff, sentences and paragraphs*

Chatty, informal, mention other stuff that shows we are friends

> Write a letter to a friend in which you argue for your choice of destination for a holiday you are going on together.   (24 marks)

Action holiday — not normal beach stuff

Recognise their point of view — mock it?! Offer counter arguments — why sun and surf not good idea — be persuasive at end

Paragraph 1: *Say I want to go on action holiday*
- *do things like abseiling, climbing, rafting*
- *get fit*
- *have a laugh*

Paragraph 2: *Good things about beach holiday*
- *relaxing*
- *good tan*
- *parties*

Paragraph 3: *Why not beach holiday*
- *boring*
- *everyone does it*
- *not an experience*

Paragraph 4: *The good things about action*
- *new experience*
- *push yourself*
- *get a tan too*

Opening line: *I know you want a beach hol, mate, but let's think about the possibilities of an all action getaway!*

Closing line: *You don't really want all of this lying around business, come and really live at a fast pace!*

Plan _____ is most compelling because…

_____

_____

_____

Plan 2

Not too quick: full sentences – developing an idea

Some sense of knowing each other – more persuasive if friendly tone but not too informal

> Write a letter to a friend in which you argue for your choice of destination for a holiday you are going on together. (24 marks)

Action holiday to test our character, not beach holiday where we would get bored and be silly

Stress the growth they will experience because of action holiday – make them a better person even

Paragraph 1: Quality of the friend you admire but...
- openness
- fun loving
- but reserved, not confident

Paragraph 3: Need to relax
- accept that beach holiday will help them relax
- but doing something different good too
- change better

Paragraph 2: Holiday is an opportunity
- push past fears
- try something new
- meet interesting people

Paragraph 4: Describe the holiday
- the laughs as they try to raft down a river
- the pride as you abseil
- the release of aggression and so relax

Opening line: You are imagining the warmth of the sun and the cool lapping of the sea, I would guess.

Closing line: Why bother with the same old sun, sea and sand... come and play – it will make you feel so very different than before!

⭐ **ResultsPlus**
Build your skills

Fill in the RAG table below to see how your confidence has improved in the following areas:

	R	A	G
I know how to analyse a question in order to understand what choices to make	○	○	○
I know how to organise ideas effectively and create a paragraph plan	○	○	○
I know how to use structure and vocabulary to write an engaging and compelling opening sentence.	○	○	○

6 Developing and sustaining an idea

I need to:

- understand which ideas would be most appropriate for the task
- understand how to use a small number of ideas and develop them fully.

This lesson will help you to produce an answer that will develop a few ideas effectively. You may be brimming over with lots of different points but to capture your reader's attention and sustain their interest you need to present them with a few well developed ideas rather than a huge list of unrelated points.

ResultsPlus
Build your skills

Fill in the RAG table below to show how confident you are in the following areas:

	R	A	G
I can select the best ideas for the audience and purpose	○	○	○
I can select ideas that will work well together	○	○	○
I can fully develop an idea	○	○	○
I can move between ideas effectively	○	○	○

Activity 1

10 MINS

Here is a sample examination question:

> Write the text for a website in which you argue that we do or do not treat animals in a humane way.
>
> (24 marks)

Below and opposite are two different responses to this question.

1. Read the two paragraphs and highlight each idea the students present.

2. In a different colour, highlight where the students have given additional details about their ideas.

Student A

British people on the whole like to think we are animal lovers. I wonder if this is true. We do enjoy owning pets and we pamper them. We also like to think we farm animals in a humane way. We are also proud when we look at bottles of shampoo to check if it was tested on animals or on the side of tins to see if dolphins were caught whilst the tuna was slaughtered. In reality we use animals for our own amusement and think a small hint of kindness makes up for the underlying cruelty in our actions.

Student B

British people on the whole like to think we are animal lovers. I wonder if this is true. We do enjoy owning pets. Look carefully at how our culture pampers its pooches and caresses its kittens. The pet industry is a multi-billionaire economic marvel. We buy little jackets, diamond-encrusted collars and give our pets homes that would make many humans jealous. Does this make us kind to animals? Or have we just enslaved animals and called them 'domestic' because it suits our needs. No dog was ever built by nature to sit on a cushion and look regal. They are meant for hunting and burrowing and guarding. Cats are brutal hunters; just ask my local bird population. How much credibility will Trixibelle have in the killing fields with a ribbon in her hair?

3 Think about how each student has approached the question. Decide:

   a which student develops their ideas better. Give reasons for your choice.

   b how each student could continue their answer.

Activity 2

20 MINS

Here is another examination question:

> Write an article for your school website in which you explain the importance of fashion and clothing to teenagers. (24 marks)

You could talk about the following in a response to this question:

manufacturing process	uniform	fashion
freedom	identity	clothes industry
personality	comfort	what to wear when growing older

1 Which of the above ideas would be most appropriate for the audience and purpose you have been given? Explain your choices.

_____

_____

_____

_____

2 Select one of the ideas you listed in Question 1. Make a list of all the issues you could explore using just this one idea.

_____

_____

_____

_____

_____

_____

_____

Producing a top band piece of writing is not about including all the ideas in your answer. It is about choosing an interesting approach to the question. Look at this example:

Key idea to focus on: Identity

Approach: To explore how clothes reveal the person underneath. Discuss how forcing people to wear uniform means hiding who we really are.

3 Select a key idea from the list you created in Question 1 and decide what approach would be most interesting and imaginative.

It is important when writing that you understand what conclusion you want the reader to reach by the end of your piece. You then need to think how you are going to guide them to this conclusion.

Look at this flow diagram which guides the reader to the conclusion made earlier about identity:

Clothes are just bits of material, perhaps it doesn't matter what we wear?

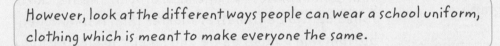

However, look at the different ways people can wear a school uniform, clothing which is meant to make everyone the same.

Look at the different approaches people take to clothing in general — an expression of personal identity.

Uniform means we are overly guided and uncomfortable — we should be allowed to express our identity through clothing.

4 Produce a flow diagram that will guide the reader to the conclusion you decided on in Question 3.

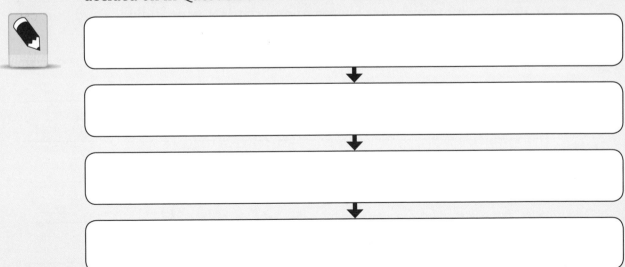

Activity 3

18 MINS

Look at these two paragraphs on clothing and identity.

Opening sentence that reveals to the reader the approach that the writer is going to take.

> It is a strange truth that our attitudes to clothing are revealed by the clothes that we wear. You can argue that clothes are just bits of material that keep us warm or cool or protected. It could also be true to suggest that we don't reveal ourselves, we reveal the person we are told to be. There is school uniform for instance and all the fashion magazines that clone us. But, doesn't this make us all sound weak and uninspired?

A series of points that open up the issue under debate – this is a good strategy in an introduction as it presents the ideas that the writer is going to explore.

Use of a question that sets up the issues in the next paragraph. This is a skilful use of paragraphing.

> Let's take the school uniform that we are all told to wear each day. To be fair it is intended to make us all look the same for whatever reason the teachers want to put forward: school community, making us different to them, conformity, pushing rules onto us for their own sake... Who knows. But, do you really look exactly like your school mates? A one inch drop of the tie, skirt rolled up two centimetres shorter than it should be, buttons and badges on tie and lapel, shirt in/shirt out, socks to knees or tights or bare legs or multi-coloured socks slightly pushing out of the shoe, blazer on or off or carelessly/purposely ripped or fitted... Everything is open to being personalised and revealing an attitude through the clothing that we wear. Is it disrespectful? Nah, it is just a small dance teenagers do with their teachers to see who breaks first!

Use of a topic sentence that uses one of the ideas presented in the introduction.

A repeated idea from the previous paragraph that makes a connection back to the overall approach being taken.

A series of examples that illustrate the original idea – showing that the point has been developed.

1 You have 15 minutes. Write the opening two paragraphs of the response to the examination question you planned in Question 4 of Activity 2. Remember to ensure your response is always appropriate for your audience and purpose.

_____

_____

_____

_____

_____

12 MINS

1 Read your paragraphs from Activity 3 critically. Ask yourself these questions:

   a Have I developed my main idea over both paragraphs?

   b Have I developed ideas using examples?

   c Have I used strategies such as topic sentences, questions and repeated key words and phrases to connect the paragraphs and ideas?

   d Is the overall approach appropriate for the audience and purpose mentioned in the examination question?

2 Label your paragraphs, showing where you have done these things.

3 Now look at the Higher Tier mark scheme below. Try to think about where you could improve your paragraphs and make edits to them or rewrite them opposite if you need to.

Band	
3	• Effectively presents ideas in a sustained way • A secure sustained realisation of the purpose of the writing task and its intended audience • Aptly chosen vocabulary and well controlled variety in the construction of sentences • Organisation is secure, with a well-judged text structure, effective paragraphing and use of cohesive devices between and within paragraphs
4	• Assured presentation of fully developed ideas • A consistent fulfilment of the writing task and assured realisation of its intended audience • Aptly chosen, reasonably extensive vocabulary and assured control in the construction of varied sentence forms • Organisation is assured, with sophisticated control of text structure, skilfully sustained paragraphing and the effective application of cohesive devices
5	• Achieves precision and clarity in presenting compelling and fully developed ideas. A strong, consistent fulfilment of the writing task sharply focused on the writer's purpose and audience • An extensive vocabulary and mature control in the construction of varied sentence forms • Organisation is convincing, with sophisticated control of text structure, skilfully sustained paragraphing and the effective application of cohesive devices

4 List what changes you have made and the reasons for these.

Fill in the RAG table below to see how your confidence has improved in the following areas:

	R	A	G
I can select the best ideas for the audience and purpose	○	○	○
I can select ideas that will work well together	○	○	○
I can fully develop an idea	○	○	○
I can move between ideas effectively	○	○	○

7 Effective word and sentence choices

I need to:
- use a variety of vocabulary appropriately and effectively
- use a variety of different sentence types appropriately and effectively.

This lesson will help you to choose words and sentences that will engage and interest your reader. Writing well is more than just communicating facts or ideas. You need to learn how to make an appropriate and effective impact on your reader. Choosing vocabulary, sentence structures and punctuation for a particular effect is crucial.

ResultsPlus
Build your skills

Fill in the RAG table below to show how confident you are in the following areas:

	R	A	G
I can choose words that are appropriate to audience and purpose	○	○	○
I can choose sentences that are appropriate to audience and purpose	○	○	○
I can choose vocabulary to make an impact on the reader	○	○	○
I can use different kinds of sentences to make an impact on the reader	○	○	○
I can use punctuation to make an impact on the reader	○	○	○

Activity 1

10 MINS

Here is a sample examination question:

> Write a the text for a speech to be given to parents in which you advise them of the many pressures on teenagers today and explain what help they need from parents. (24 marks)

1 Complete this paragraph by circling the highlighted word that you think is most appropriate for the audience and purpose.

Your kids'/children's/teenagers' experience is incredibly/very different from what you lived through just a few years ago. Each day they are pushed/pressured/encouraged to work and behave in certain ways that you most likely have never imagined/believed/considered. School is all about results, friends are all about the right code of behaviour and family is about being cared for whilst seeming to be mature/grown up/ independent. There is no place where your kids/children/teenagers can relax, as they are always being judged/tested/pressured.

2 Edit the following paragraph so that the vocabulary is more appropriate for the audience and purpose. Rewrite sections where appropriate.

> Take the example of friendships. When you were a kid there was no Facebook, no Twitter, no MySpace. While all of these things can be hugely beneficial and fun, they can also add to the pressures on us and no mistake. Back in the day you could go out for an evening safe in the knowledge that there wouldn't be pictures of you on Facebook the next morning. Or worse still, videos of you attempting to dance and not looking as cool as you thought you did.

Activity 2

20 MINS

When selecting words and sentences to have a particular impact you need to decide what reaction you would like from your audience. Do you want them to feel guilty, sad, angry, thoughtful or amused? Do you want them to act on your words or do you just want them to feel informed?

1 Look at these sample examination questions. What would be an effective reaction from the audience?

	Sample examination question	Audience reaction
1	Write a letter to a friend persuading them to seek help rather than run away.	
2	Write a magazine article in which you argue for or against the value of reality TV programmes.	
3	Write an article for a lifestyle magazine in which you discuss the benefits and drawbacks of modern technology	
4	Write a speech for your local community in which you review the facilities available to young people in the local area.	
5	Write a letter to a friend in which you describe your recent experiences on holiday.	

2 Look at the two paragraphs opposite, which are written in response to two of the sample examination questions above. Some key language choices have been highlighted.

a What techniques has the writer used in each paragraph? Select from the techniques in the box and use them to label the highlighted words in each paragraph. You can use more than one technique each time.

> emotive language   hyperbole   rhetorical question   exclamation
>
> single-word sentence   ellipsis   technical vocabulary   compounding
>
> repetition   listing   slang   direct address   direct speech

b Explain what impact the writer hoped to have in each paragraph.

Paragraph A

Paragraph B

Paragraph A (sample examination question 1)

Does it feel like you are caught in a stormy glass cage? You are not alone. There are people everywhere, but you feel so isolated and trapped! It is human nature to want to take control and I realise you are compelled to do something, anything, to get away from the pain you are feeling. Can I ask you something? Please wait.

Paragraph B (sample examination question 3)

Genius! I've just discovered how I can talk to my cousin in Australia face-to face online … and for free! OK, maybe not face-to-face, but she can see me and I can see her via video link, using an easy and widely available piece of software and a webcam. Yes, it is addictive. Yes, it does take up big chunks of the day unless I drag myself away from the computer. And yes, the conversations aren't strictly necessary. But hey, what is more satisfying than a show-and-tell conversation with someone important who happens to be on the other side of the world?

3 Write a paragraph for one of the other examination questions opposite. Underline key language choices you have made to suit the audience and purpose. Label the paragraph with the reasons for these choices.

Activity 3

20 MINS

To write effective sentences you need to use punctuation wisely. You can create specific effects just by using different punctuation.

1 The extracts below are alternative concluding paragraphs from a piece in which a student gives her thoughts about homework. However, each has been written for a different audience and purpose.

a Read each extract. Highlight all the punctuation that is different in each paragraph.

Extract A

> We have seen that homework is time-consuming for teachers, stressful for students and is not always a helpful learning exercise. So ask yourself: what is the point of homework? In my opinion, there isn't one. Surely we would be better off spending our free time having fun, playing sport, seeing our friends and relaxing. It would help us to conserve our mental energy for paying attention during the school day. Honestly, the best solution is to ban homework.

Extract B

> We have seen that homework is time-consuming for teachers, stressful for students and is not always a helpful learning exercise. So ask yourself: what is the point of homework? In my opinion, there isn't one! Surely we would be better off spending our free time having fun, playing sport, seeing our friends and relaxing. It would help us to 'conserve our mental energy' for paying attention during the school day... Honestly! The best solution is to ban homework.

b Can you identify the audience and purpose of each extract?

Extract A audience: _____

Extract A purpose: _____

Extract B audience: _____

Extract B purpose: _____

c Read the extracts again, paying particular attention to the punctuation. Think about the tone of each paragraph. Which is more light-hearted? Which is more formal? Explain how the punctuation has achieved this effect.

_____

_____

_____

_____

2 The paragraph below is about the fitness activities young people might enjoy in the local area of Holmethorpe.

Does it ever seem like there's not much to do well actually Holmethorpe is packed full of surprising activities if you look for them whenever you next feel bored check out the local sports club that runs all kinds of classes from football to dance and from cross-country to boules even javelin-throwing is on the agenda if you're feeling very adventurous take a visit to the climbing wall where you can get a reduced young-person rate for an hour of clambering with a personal instructor guaranteed to get you active

Rewrite the paragraph, using punctuation that will make the paragraph suitable for the following audience, purpose and form.

Form: A teenage magazine available in the local area
Audience: Other young people in Holmethorpe
Purpose: To describe the activities that are available and encourage other young people to get fit

_____

_____

_____

_____

_____

Here is a sample examination question:

> Write a review for the school magazine focused on a recent school event such as a sports team's performance or a recent production. (24 marks)

1 Match the sentences to the partial descriptions for the top three mark bands.

Band	Description	Sentences
3	Aptly chosen vocabulary and well controlled variety of in the construction of sentences.	Sports Day: an afternoon on the field with ice lollies and your mates, cheering on your form. It doesn't get better than this! Well, it would be infinitely better if it hadn't rained and my form had won...
4	Aptly chosen, reasonably extensive vocabulary and assured control in the construction of varied sentence forms.	We had a great time on the afternoon of Sports Day. My favourite memory was watching Mr Davies skipping happily down the track at the end of races cheering on the stragglers.
5	An extensive vocabulary and mature control in the construction of sentences.	Her hair trailed behind her... her arms punched powerfully... her face: effortless. Time slowed — it was like the slow motion dramatics of an old movie. The record was smashed! Lennox modestly raised an arm and blushed shyly as she was photographed from all angles.

2 Here is a Band 3 paragraph. Edit the vocabulary and sentence choices so that it can achieve a better mark. Write your improved paragraph opposite.

> The award ceremony was an exciting end to the day. All the students and staff crowded around as Mrs Sawar and Mr Scutt read out the winners. There were cheers and some quiet grumbles as the same Year 10 form won for the fourth year running. It started to rain again and the wind got up, so Mr Scutt sent us all back into school to wait for the bell. A good afternoon and we would like to thank the PE Department.

_____

_____

_____

_____

_____

_____

_____

_____

_____

3   Ask a partner to assess your paragraph to see if it has achieved a Band 4 or 5. Ask your partner to talk you through the reasons for their decision, making reference to the mark scheme descriptions opposite.

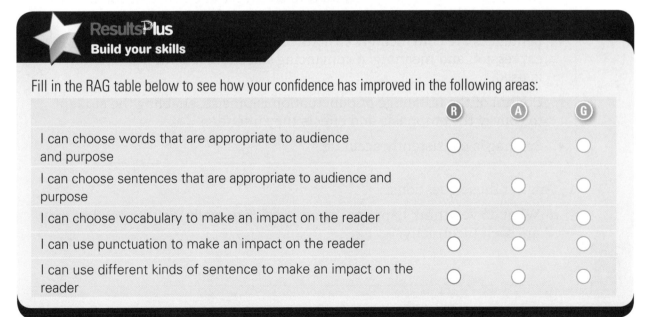

ResultsPlus
Build your skills

Fill in the RAG table below to see how your confidence has improved in the following areas:

	R	A	G
I can choose words that are appropriate to audience and purpose	○	○	○
I can choose sentences that are appropriate to audience and purpose	○	○	○
I can choose vocabulary to make an impact on the reader	○	○	○
I can use punctuation to make an impact on the reader	○	○	○
I can use different kinds of sentence to make an impact on the reader	○	○	○

8 Crafting and editing

I need to:
- make accurate language choices
- check that choices are effective and appropriate.

This lesson will help you to practise checking over your work. The difference between one grade and another might be a matter of a couple of marks. You need to spend some time during the writing process checking back and making sure silly errors don't cost you the mark you deserve!

ResultsPlus
Build your skills

Fill in the RAG table below to show how confident you are in the following areas:

	R	A	G
I know how to check my spelling	○	○	○
I know how to ensure my sentences are accurate	○	○	○
I understand how to craft vocabulary and sentence choices	○	○	○
I can evaluate my response using what I know about the mark scheme	○	○	○

Activity 1

10 MINS

Look at these extracts from the Higher Tier mark scheme. They show some of the criteria for obtaining a mark in the top band.

- An extensive vocabulary and mature control in the construction of varied sentence forms.

- Sentences are convincingly structured, with sophisticated control of expression and meaning. A convincing selection of sentence structures is used.

- Control of the full range of punctuation is precise, enabling the student to convey the emphasis and effects they intended.

- Spelling is consistently accurate.

1   Answer these questions:

   a   What do you think happens if your words are really well chosen but they are spelt incorrectly?

_____

_____

b What do you think happens if you are attempting to use different punctuation and sentence structures but sometimes you get it wrong?

_____

c Which does the mark scheme value more: accuracy or ambition?

_____

2 Write two paragraphs in response to the following sample examination question:

> Write a letter to your local MP suggesting how your neighbourhood could be improved for young people.　　　　　　　　(24 marks)

In Paragraph 1 you should write so that you are certain everything is accurate. In Paragraph 2 you should write using well chosen, ambitious vocabulary and sentence structures.

_____

_____

_____

_____

_____

_____

_____

_____

_____

_____

3 Check the two paragraphs against the mark scheme. Discuss the consequences of these two approaches with your teacher and/or a partner.

Activity 2

In an examination, it is important to check your spelling. You should:

- check words that you know you often get wrong, especially under pressure
- sound out words you are unsure how to spell.

1 Look through some of your written work from school. Make a list of all the words that your teacher has marked as being spelt incorrectly.

_____

_____

_____

_____

_____

_____

_____

2 Look at the spelling errors closely. Is there a pattern? For instance, some people struggle with homophones such as _there_, _their_ and _they're_. Some people find it difficult to remember whether to use double consonants, for example in words such as _possession_ or _fulfil_. Make a note of any patterns below and add any extra words which you find difficult.

_____

_____

_____

_____

_____

_____

_____

_____

3 Look closely at this list of most commonly misspelt words.

address	guarantee	occurrence
advice	harass	piece
beginning	humorous	prejudice
believe	independent	privilege
changeable	jealous	receive
conscientious	knowledge	rhythm
conscious	leisure	separate
deceive	library	sincerely
definite	mediocre	special
desperate	miniature	surprise
disastrous	miscellaneous	thorough
embarrass	mischievous	through
fascinate	mysterious	truly
fiery	necessary	until
government	neighbour	weird
grateful	occasion	

a Highlight any interesting words that you think you would be able to use in a piece of writing.

b Tick any word that you know you can spell.

c Add any word that is not ticked to the list that you created in Question 2.

4 Choose a word from the list above that you would not normally use. Try to write a sentence using the word. Check the meaning in the dictionary if you are not sure. Repeat the process for two other words on the list.

1 _____

_____

2 _____

_____

3 _____

_____

5 Produce a bookmark and write all the words that you need to pay special attention to onto one side of the bookmark. Use the bookmark in a book that you use all the time.

Good writing is about rhythm, flow and tone. Put simply, you need to check that your writing 'sounds good'. The best way to do this is to read your writing aloud. In the examination, you will have to read it over in your head!

Activity 3

20 MINS

1 Read the sample examination question below, then read the extract from a response aloud. Highlight places where the text sounds clumsy or a word doesn't seem appropriate.

> Write an article for the local newspaper in which you review the different facilities available to young people in your local area. **(24 marks)**

This is not really a town that is bustling majorly with opportunity for young people such as me. There are a number of colleges I can go to and they all offer good courses but at the end of the day they offer the same things — just in different places. It seems that the only way to succeed in this world is to go and do even more qualifications in subjects that require you to write lots and remember even more. I don't see the point. I am never going to be majorly academic so what I will do is a major mystery.

2 Rewrite the paragraph to overcome the problems you have highlighted. Keep reading the text out loud until you can read it without pausing or stumbling over words or sentences.

_____

_____

_____

_____

_____

_____

_____

_____

3 Write a paragraph of your own in response to the sample examination question. Read the paragraph silently but try to 'hear' the words in your head. Edit the paragraph until you can read it without pausing or stumbling over things that do not sound quite right.

20 MINS

1 Here is a sample examination question:

> Write the text for a leaflet persuading people that they should support a charity you feel strongly about. **(24 marks)**

You have ten minutes. Write as much as you can in response to this question.

_____

_____

_____

_____

_____

_____

_____

_____

_____

_____

_____

_____

_____

_____

_____

_____

_____

2 Read your response. Highlight all the inaccuracies in spelling. Now, in a different colour, highlight all the words where you could have made a better choice. In another colour highlight sentences that seem lazy or don't read well.

3 Make changes in the margin and re-read your paragraph.

4 The final step in checking your response is to think about the mark scheme and decide whether your answer is as good as it could be.

Ask yourself:

- Will your writing engage your audience? Will they react in the way you want them to? ☐

- Does your writing fulfil its purpose? ☐

- Are your ideas interesting and original? ☐

- Is your writing well structured? Have you used paragraphs? ☐

- Have you used a wide range of vocabulary and sentences? ☐

- Is your punctuation accurate? ☐

If the answer is 'No' to any of these questions, you need to make changes.

ResultsPlus
Build your skills

Fill in the RAG table below to see how your confidence has improved in the following areas.

	R	A	G
I know how to check my spelling	○	○	○
I know how to ensure my sentences are accurate	○	○	○
I understand how to craft vocabulary and sentence choices	○	○	○
I can evaluate my response using what I know about the mark scheme	○	○	○

1 Responding to characters

I need to:

- **show that I have a perceptive understanding of character**
- **use a variety of discriminating evidence from the text to demonstrate my knowledge about a character.**

This lesson will help you to prepare for the Section A Literary Heritage question in your Unit 1 Literature examination. There are four parts to the question:

- **Part (a)** will ask you to comment on what you learn about a character in an extract.
- **Part (b)** will ask you to comment on the use of language in an extract.
- **Part (c)** will ask you to comment on the importance of a character, relationship, setting or theme in the extract.
- **Part (d)** will ask you to explore the importance of a character, relationship, setting or theme in one other part of the text.

This lesson will focus on **part (a)** of the question – commenting on what you discover about a character in an extract that you are given from the text you have studied.

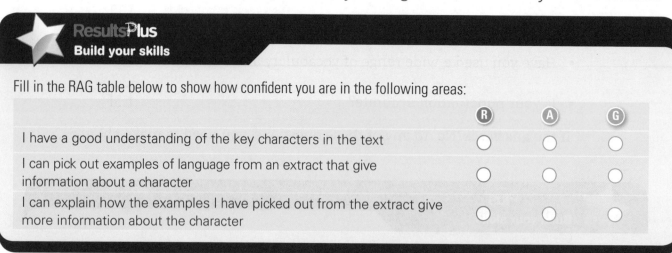

ResultsPlus
Build your skills

Fill in the RAG table below to show how confident you are in the following areas:

	R	A	G
I have a good understanding of the key characters in the text	○	○	○
I can pick out examples of language from an extract that give information about a character	○	○	○
I can explain how the examples I have picked out from the extract give more information about the character	○	○	○

Activity 1

10 MINS

It is important to have a general understanding of the characters in the text in order to be able to comment on the presentation of a character within an extract for **part (a)**.

1   Choose one of the main characters in the text you have studied and complete their character profile opposite. The evidence you select might be something which a character does or says, or the language that is used by the writer to describe him or her. Remember that you won't be asked to complete an exercise like this in the examination. This activity will just help you to reinforce your knowledge of the text so that you are able to comment effectively on an extract in the examination.

a Name: _____

b In the table below, list three character traits and provide evidence from the text to support each of them.

	Character trait	Evidence from the text
1		
2		
3		

c What happens to this character in the text? Outline the key events in which they are involved. This will help you to think about the different extracts in which they are presented.

_____
_____
_____
_____

d Why is this character important in the text? Support your answer with examples from the text.

_____
_____
_____
_____
_____

In the examination, when you write about how a character is presented in an extract, you need to give 'discriminating examples' from the extract. This means that you need to ensure your examples really help to support the point you are making.

Activity 2

15 MINS

In this activity you will explain what you discover about a character from the evidence in the extract. Some 'discriminating examples' have been chosen for you.

1 Complete the table for the text you have studied to explore what we learn about either Napoleon (*Animal Farm*) or Hyde (*Dr Jekyll and Mr Hyde*) from the extract. One answer has been filled in for you.

Animal Farm, Chapter 3, pages 15–16

After a little thought the pigs sent for buckets and milked the cows fairly successfully, their trotters being well adapted to this task. Soon there were five buckets of frothing creamy milk at which many of the animals looked with considerable interest.

'What is going to happen to all that milk?' said someone.

'Jones used sometimes to mix some of it in our mash,' said one of the hens.

'Never mind the milk, comrades,' cried Napoleon, placing himself in front of the buckets. 'That will be attended to. The harvest is more important. Comrade Snowball will lead the way. I shall follow in a few minutes. Forward, comrades! The hay is waiting.'

So the animals trooped down to the hayfield to begin the harvest, and when they came back in the evening it was noticed that the milk had disappeared.

Evidence	What we learn about the character
'Never mind the milk, comrades!'	
'That will be attended to.'	
'I shall follow in a few minutes.'	Napoleon finds it easy to dupe the other animals. Ironically, Napoleon never 'follows' but leads. At this stage in the text the animals are not aware of his duplicity.
'Forward, comrades! The hay is waiting.'	
...and when they came back in the evening it was noticed that the milk had disappeared.	

Dr Jekyll and Mr Hyde, 'Story of the Door', page 7

All at once, I saw two figures: one a little man who was stumping along eastward at a good walk, and the other a girl of maybe eight or ten who was running as hard as she was able down a cross street. Well, sir, the two ran into one another naturally enough at the corner; and then came the horrible part of the thing; for the man trampled calmly over the child's body and left her screaming on the ground. It sounds nothing to hear, but it was hellish to see. It wasn't like a man; it was like some damned Juggernaut. I gave a view halloa, took to my heels, collared my gentleman, and brought him back to where there was already quite a group about the screaming child. He was perfectly cool and made no resistance, but gave me one look, so ugly that it brought out the sweat on me like running.

Evidence	What we learn about the character
a little man who was stumping along eastwards at a good walk	
the man trampled calmly over the child's body and left her screaming on the ground	
It wasn't like a man; it was like some damned Juggernaut.	The simile comparing him to a truck suggests that he is not human and does not have the ability to judge how bad his behaviour is. Even when he knows that people are shocked by his behaviour, he doesn't care. This is an example of his amorality.
He was perfectly cool and made no resistance	
but gave me one look, so ugly that it brought out the sweat on me like running	

Activity 3

1 Read the short extract from your chosen text below. Annotate the extract to show what the highlighted phrases tell you about the character of **either** Squealer **or** Utterson.

Animal Farm, Chapter 5, page 35

Afterwards Squealer was sent round the farm to explain the new arrangement to the others.

'Comrades,' he said, 'I trust that every animal here appreciates the sacrifice that Comrade Napoleon has made in taking this extra labour upon himself. Do not imagine, comrade, that leadership is a pleasure! On the contrary, it is a deep and heavy responsibility. No one believes more firmly that Comrade Napoleon that all animals are equal. He would be only too happy to let you make your decisions for yourselves. But sometimes you might make the wrong decisions, comrades, and then where should we be? Suppose you had decided to follow Snowball, with his moonshine of windmills – Snowball, who, as we now know, was no better than a criminal?'

'He fought bravely at the Battle of the Cowshed,' said somebody.

'Bravery is not enough,' said Squealer. 'Loyalty and obedience are more important. And as to the Battle of the Cowshed, I believe the time will come when we shall find that Snowball's part in it was much exaggerated. Discipline, comrades, iron discipline!'

Dr Jekyll and Mr Hyde, 'Search for Mr Hyde', page 14

From that time forward, Mr Utterson began to haunt the door in the bystreet of shops. In the morning before office hours, at noon when business was plenty and time scarce, at night under the face of the fogged city moon, by all lights and at all hours of solitude or concourse, the lawyer was to be found on his chosen post.

'If he be Mr Hyde,' he had thought, 'I shall be Mr Seek'.

And at last his patience was rewarded. It was a fine dry night; frost in the air; the streets as clean as a ballroom floor; the lamps, unshaken by any wind, drawing a regular pattern of light and shadow. By ten o'clock, when the shops were closed, the bystreet was very solitary and, in spite of the low growl of London from all round, very silent. Small sounds carried far; domestic sounds out of the houses were clearly audible on either side of the roadway; and the rumour of the approach of any passenger preceded him by a long time. Mr Utterson had been some minutes at his post, when he was aware of an odd, light footstep drawing near. In the course of his nightly patrols, he had long grown accustomed to the quaint effect with which the footfalls of a single person, while he is still a great way off, suddenly spring out distinct from the vast hum and clatter of the city.

2   Write one paragraph in response to the following sample examination question:

> From the extract, what do you discover about the character of Squealer (*Animal Farm*) or Utterson (*Dr Jekyll and Mr Hyde*)?
>
> Use evidence from the extract to support your answer.   (8 marks)

1 In this activity you will assess a student's work that has been written in response to the sample examination question in Activity 3. Using the Higher Tier mark scheme, say which band you think the student would achieve and explain the reasons for your decision.

Animal Farm

In the first sentence we learn that in this extract Squealer will 'explain the new arrangement' to the animals. However, what he says is less of an explanation and more of a persuasive speech which is designed to influence the animals, which makes him seem quite cunning and manipulative. He uses the word 'comrades' repeatedly to try and establish a good relationship, but he also uses phrases such as 'I trust that every animal here appreciates the sacrifice Comrade Napoleon has made...' to make it seem as if this is obvious and they should be thankful to Napoleon for taking away their ability to make decisions. He also uses commands such as 'Do not imagine...' followed by an exclamation mark to suggest how ridiculous the idea of power being a pleasure really is. This clearly gives an impression of him being a clever character who is fully in control of the situation.

Dr Jekyll and Mr Hyde

In this extract, the reader gets an impression of Utterson as a dedicated, curious man. The verb 'haunt' to describe his actions shows how frequently he remains on the lookout for Mr Hyde, and also suggests he is quite a mysterious character. The long second sentence in the first paragraph, with phrases separated by commas, and ending in 'by all lights and at all hours of solitude or concourse, the lawyer was to be found on his chosen post' also shows his persistence. The one line of speech he has also shows he is quite clever, using a pun on the name of Mr Hyde.

This Higher Tier mark scheme will be used to mark your examination response.

Band	Description
1	• Generally sound or sound understanding of the character • Uses relevant evidence from the extract to demonstrate knowledge about the character
2	• Thorough understanding of the character • Uses a good range of evidence from the extract to demonstrate knowledge about the character
3	• Perceptive understanding of the character • Uses a variety of discriminating evidence from the extract to demonstrate knowledge about the character

The student would gain a Band _____ because _____

_____

_____

2 For Activity 3 question 2 you wrote a paragraph of a response to a sample examination question. Look again at your answer and use the Higher Tier mark scheme above to assess your work. Alternatively, you could swap your work with a partner and mark each other's work. Say which band you think the answer would achieve and justify your decisions, referring to the band criteria.

_____

_____

_____

ResultsPlus
Build your skills

Fill in the RAG table below to see how your confidence has improved in the following areas:

	R	A	G
I have a good understanding of the key characters in the text	○	○	○
I can pick out examples of language from an extract that give information about a character	○	○	○
I can explain how the examples I have picked out from the extract give more information about the character	○	○	○

2 Responding to the writer's use of language

I need to:

- explain how the writer achieves effects with their use of language
- demonstrate understanding of linguistic, grammatical, structural and presentational features of language
- give relevant examples to support my points.

This lesson will help you to prepare for the Section A Literary Heritage question in your examination. The lesson will focus on **part (b)** of the question, which will ask you to comment on the effect of the language used within an extract to present a character, relationship, event, idea, theme or setting.

ResultsPlus
Build your skills

Fill in the RAG table below to show how confident you are in the following areas:

	R	A	G
I can explain how the writer uses language to present their ideas	○	○	○
I can comment on the effect of particular language features and techniques	○	○	○
I can select relevant examples from the text to support my points	○	○	○

Activity 1

15 MINS

The best answers make convincing, intelligent points about the text and are supported by the best, most relevant examples.

1 Read the extract from your chosen text which follows. Annotate the highlighted examples in the extract to explain how they present the power of the pigs (*Animal Farm*) or build up a sense of the atmosphere (*Dr Jekyll and Mr Hyde*).

Animal Farm,
Chapter 7, pages 47–48

When the hens heard this they raised a terrible outcry. They had been warned earlier that this sacrifice might be necessary, but had not believed that it would really happen. They were just getting their clutches ready for the spring sitting, and they protested that to take the eggs away now was murder. For the first time since the expulsion of Jones there was something resembling a rebellion.

Led by three young black Minorca pullets, the hens made a determined effort to thwart Napoleon's wishes. Their method was to fly up to the rafters and there lay their eggs, which smashed to pieces on the floor. Napoleon acted swiftly and ruthlessly. He ordered the hens' rations to be stopped, and decreed that any animal giving as much as a grain of corn to a hen should be punished by death. The dogs saw to it that these orders were carried out. For five days the hens held out, then they capitulated and went back to their nesting boxes. Nine hens had died in the meantime.

Dr Jekyll and Mr Hyde, 'Incident of the Letter', page 26

It was the first time that the lawyer had been received in that part of his friend's quarters; and he eyed the dingy, windowless structure with curiosity, and gazed round with a distasteful sense of strangeness as he crossed the theatre, once crowded with eager students and now lying gaunt and silent, the tables laden with chemical apparatus, the floor strewn with crates and littered with packing straw, and the light falling dimly through the foggy cupola. At the further end, a flight of stairs mounted to a door covered with red baize; and through this, Mr Utterson was at last received into the doctor's cabinet. It was a large room, fitted round with glass presses, furnished, among other things, with a cheval-glass and a business table, and looking out upon the court by three dusty windows barred with iron. A fire burned in the grate; a lamp was set lighted on the chimney shelf, for even in the houses the fog began to lie thickly; and there, close up to the warmth, sat Dr Jekyll, looking deadly sick. He did not rise to meet his visitor, but held out a cold hand and bade him welcome in a changed voice.

Activity 2

1 Read the short extract from your chosen text along with the sample examination question. Then complete the sentences to comment on the language in the extract.

Animal Farm, Chapter 5, pages 33–34

> Silent and terrified, the animals crept back into the barn. In a moment the dogs came bounding back. At first no one had been able to imagine where these creatures came from, but the problem was soon solved: they were the puppies whom Napoleon has taken away from their mothers and reared privately. Though not yet full-grown, they were huge dogs and as fierce-looking as wolves. They kept close to Napoleon. It was noticed that they wagged their tails to him in the same way as the other dogs had been used to do to Mr. Jones.

> Comment on the effect of the language used to create an impression of the dogs in this extract. Use examples of the writer's language from the extract.
>
> (10 marks)

In this extract, the dogs are deliberately contrasted with the other animals to show...

_____

The word 'bounding' suggests that the dogs are...

_____

In contrast, the behaviour of the other animals is...

_____

They are described as 'silent and terrified' and we are told that they 'crept back into the barn', emphasising...

_____

Dr Jekyll and Mr Hyde, 'Dr Jekyll was Quite at Ease', pages 19–20

The large handsome face of Dr Jekyll grew pale to the very lips, and there came a blackness about his eyes. 'I do not care to hear more,' said he. 'This is a matter I thought we had agreed to drop.'

'What I heard was abominable,' said Utterson.

'It can make no change. You do not understand my position,' returned the doctor, with a certain incoherency of manner. 'I am painfully situated, Utterson; my position is a very strange – a very strange one. It is one of those affairs that cannot be mended by talking.'

Comment on the effect of the language used to present Dr Jekyll in this extract. Use examples of the writer's language from the extract.

(10 marks)

The description of Jekyll's reaction to the mention of Hyde shows...

_____

Although normally 'handsome', he becomes pale, which...

_____

The word 'blackness' suggests...

_____

His behaviour is odd and his manner is described as having a 'certain incoherency', which suggests...

_____

2   Now write three bullet points to sum up the main points you would make in answer to the sample examination question, based on the language you have commented on and any other language in the extract you think is relevant.

_____

_____

_____

Activity 3

20 MINS

In this activity you will write two paragraphs about how the writer has used language in a given extract.

1 Read the sample examination question and the extract from the text that you have studied. Write two paragraphs in response to the question. A suggested start to your response has been offered. You will need to continue your response on a separate sheet of paper.

Animal Farm, Chapter 5, page 35

> Comment on how language is used to create an impression of Napoleon. Use examples of the writer's language from the extract. (10 marks)

Afterwards Squealer was sent round the farm to explain the new arrangement to the others.

'Comrades,' he said, 'I trust that every animal here appreciates the sacrifice that Comrade Napoleon has made in taking this extra labour upon himself. Do not imagine, comrade, that leadership is a pleasure! On the contrary, it is a deep and heavy responsibility. No one believes more firmly than Comrade Napoleon that all animals are equal. He would be only too happy to let you make your decisions for yourselves. But sometimes you might make the wrong decisions, comrades, and then where should we be? Suppose you had decided to follow Snowball, with his moonshine of windmills – Snowball, who, as we now know, was no better than a criminal?'

'He fought bravely at the Battle of the Cowshed,' said somebody.

'Bravery is not enough,' said Squealer. 'Loyalty and obedience are more important. And as to the Battle of the Cowshed, I believe the time will come when we shall find that Snowball's part in it was much exaggerated. Discipline, comrades, iron discipline!

In this extract, Squealer directly addresses the animals repeatedly using the word 'Comrades' to build up a sense of trust and friendship. His tone is persuasive and commanding as he aims to build up a picture of Napoleon, as he uses....

Dr Jekyll and Mr Hyde, 'Search for Mr Hyde', page 14

Comment on the effect of the language used to create suspense in the extract.
Use examples of the writer's language from the extract.   (10 marks)

From that time forward, Mr Utterson began to haunt the door in the bystreet of shops. In the morning before office hours, at noon when business was plenty and time scarce, at night under the face of the fogged city moon, by all lights and at all hours of solitude or concourse, the lawyer was to be found on his chosen post.

'If he be Mr Hyde,' he had thought, 'I shall be Mr Seek'.

And at last his patience was rewarded. It was a fine dry night; frost in the air; the streets as clean as a ballroom floor; the lamps, unshaken by any wind, drawing a regular pattern of light and shadow. By ten o'clock, when the shops were closed, the bystreet was very solitary and, in spite of the low growl of London from all round, very silent. Small sounds carried far; domestic sounds out of the houses were clearly audible on either side of the roadway; and the rumour of the approach of any passenger preceded him by a long time. Mr Utterson had been some minutes at his post, when he was aware of an odd, light footstep drawing near. In the course of his nightly patrols, he had long grown accustomed to the quaint effect with which the footfalls of a single person, while he is still a great way off, suddenly spring out distinct from the vast hum and clatter of the city.

Stevenson creates a sense of suspense as Utterson seeks out Mr Hyde by 'haunting' the streets. We get a feel for how frequently he does this by the long sentence in the first paragraph. The first sentence of the third paragraph, 'And at last, his patience was rewarded', is particularly effective because...

_____

_____

_____

_____

ResultsPlus
Build better answers

In this activity you will assess your own work and that of another student.

1 Read through your response to Activity 3 and, using the Higher Tier mark scheme, decide on the band you would achieve. Write down the reason for your decision. Have you included in your answer possible reasons why the writer has chosen specific words? Have you explored any comparisons or contrasts made or language features used, and their effects?

I achieved a Band _____ because _____

_____

2 Now read the following student answer to the sample examination question in Activity 3. Using the mark scheme provided, decide which band it would be awarded and give a reason for this.

Animal Farm

Squealer makes several strong statements in the extract to emphasise Napoleon's good character and ensure the animals trust him. For example, the use of the comparative 'more' in the phrase 'No one believes more firmly than Comrade Napoleon that all animals are equal' adds emphasis and makes Napoleon seem outstanding. Similarly, the 'only too' in the following sentence suggests his good character and his generosity. These two statements are followed by two rhetorical questions, which Squealer uses to explain why Napoleon will not let them make their own decisions and prevent them feeling hostile towards him. The questions plant fear in their mind of making a 'wrong' decision without the guidance of Napoleon.

Dr Jekyll and Mr Hyde

Suspense is built up in this extract through use of description of the setting in which Utterson will first encounter Mr Hyde. From the very first sentence in the final paragraph of the extract, we know that Mr Hyde will appear ('At last his patience was rewarded') so the reader is waiting to know what happens. However, Stevenson spends time building up the mood. The use of adjectives to describe the dark evening such as 'fine dry night' and 'lamps, unshaken by any wind', as well as the simile 'the streets were as clean as a ballroom floor' build up an impression of a crisp, eerie atmosphere. The adjectives 'solitary' and 'silent' emphasise that, at this point, Utterson is alone, which builds up suspense as we are aware that he will soon not be. The only sound is the 'low growl of London', and this example of personification of the city is the only suggestion of an ominous, hostile, animal-like presence.

The student would achieve a Band _____ because _____

_____

This Higher Tier mark scheme will be used to mark your examination response.

Band	Description
3	• Sustained reference to how the writer achieves effects • Thorough understanding of linguistic, grammatical, structural and presentational features of language • Sustained use of relevant examples from the extract
4	• Pertinent reference to how the writer achieves effects • Assured understanding of linguistic, grammatical, structural and presentational features of language • Assured use of relevant examples from the examples
5	• Convincing reference to how the writer achieves effects • Perceptive understanding of linguistic, grammatical, structural and presentational features of language • Perceptive use of relevant examples from the extract

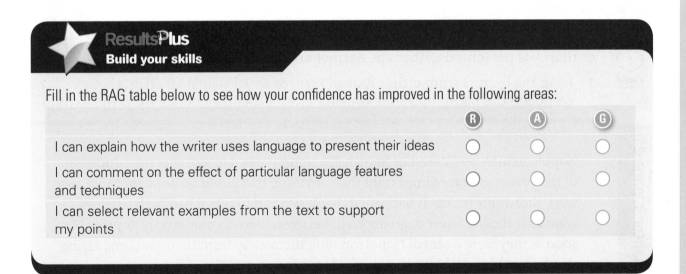

ResultsPlus
Build your skills

Fill in the RAG table below to see how your confidence has improved in the following areas:

	R	A	G
I can explain how the writer uses language to present their ideas	○	○	○
I can comment on the effect of particular language features and techniques	○	○	○
I can select relevant examples from the text to support my points	○	○	○

3 Exploring characters, relationships, events, ideas, themes and settings

I need to:

- demonstrate my knowledge of a character, relationship, event, idea, theme or setting and their significance in the novel
- show understanding of linguistic, grammatical, structural and presentational features of language
- explain how the author has used specific examples of language
- select appropriate examples of language to support my points.

This lesson will help you to prepare for **parts (c)** and **(d)** of the Section A Unit 1 English Literature question in your examination. You will be asked to explore the significance of a character, relationship, event, idea, theme or setting both within a given extract and in one other part of the text which you choose yourself.

ResultsPlus
Build your skills

Fill in the RAG table below to show how confident you are in the following areas:

	R	A	G
I have a good understanding of the key characters, relationships, themes and settings within the text and can explain their significance	○	○	○
I can explain how the writer uses language to present characters, relationships, themes and settings within an extract	○	○	○
I can select relevant examples from the text to support my points	○	○	○

Activity 1

7 MINS

In your examination you should focus on how the character, relationship, setting or theme is presented within the extract and its significance.

1 Read the extract from either *Animal Farm* or *Dr Jekyll and Mr Hyde*, then complete the paragraph that appears after it using evidence from the extract.

Animal Farm, Chapter 3, page 21

> Napoleon took no interest in Snowball's committees. He said that the education of the young was more important than anything that could be done for those who were already grown up. It happened that Jessie and Bluebell had both whelped soon after the hay harvest, giving birth between them to nine sturdy puppies. As soon as they were weaned, Napoleon took them away from their mothers, saying that he would make himself responsible for their education. He took them up into a loft which could only be reached by a ladder from the harness-room, and there kept them in such seclusion that the rest of the farm soon forgot their existence.
>
> The mystery of where the milk went to was soon cleared up. It was mixed every day into the pigs' mash.

One of the themes in *Animal Farm* is the abuse of power. This is seen immediately in this extract when Napoleon plays no part in Snowball's committees. It was not in Napoleon's interest to _____ the older animals – it was easier to keep them under control if they were _____ His view of education is actually brainwashing, and this is what he does with the _____ that he takes away from their parents. Another example of abuse of power can be seen in the pigs' exclusive use of the _____ and _____. As one of the commandments was that 'All animals are equal' it was expected by the other animals that these provisions would be shared.

Two doors from one corner, on the left hand going east, the line was broken by the entry of a court; and just at that point, a certain sinister block of building thrust forward its gable on the street. It was two stories high; showed no signs of window, nothing but a door on the lower story and a blind forehead of discoloured wall on the upper; and bore in every feature, the mark of prolonged and sordid negligence. The door, which was equipped with neither bell nor knocker, was blistered and distained.

One of the themes of *Dr Jekyll and Mr Hyde* is the link between particular settings in London and the behaviour of _____ In this extract the description of the building creates a _____ tone which echoes Hyde's behaviour. However, there is also a clear sense of neglect which hints at Jekyll's obsession with the experiments to the detriment of everything else. The building is described as a '_____ block of building' which hints at Hyde's evil and worrying behaviour. The personification of the building, which had a 'blind forehead' might be referring to Hyde's imoral _____. The adjective 'sordid' also suggests Hyde's behaviour.

Dr Jekyll and Mr Hyde, 'Story of the Door', page 6

Activity 2

15 MINS

In this activity you will think about how the writer uses language to present either the significance of power (*Animal Farm*) or the importance of the setting (*Dr Jekyll and Mr Hyde*).

1 Read the extract from the text you have studied, then answer the questions.

Animal Farm, Chapter 5, page 33

> By the time he had finished speaking there was no doubt as to which way the vote would go. But just at this moment Napoleon stood up and, casting a peculiar sidelong look at Snowball, uttered a high-pitched whimper of a kind no one had ever heard him utter before.
>
> At this there was a terrible baying sound outside, and nine enormous dogs wearing brass-studded collars came bounding into the barn. They dashed straight for Snowball, who only sprang from his place just in time to escape their snapping jaws. In a moment he was out of the door and they were after him. Too amazed and frightened to speak, all the animals crowded through the door to watch the chase. Snowball was racing across the long pasture that led to the road. He was running as only a pig can run, but the dogs were close on his heels. Suddenly he slipped and it seemed certain that they had him. Then he was up again, running faster than ever, then the dogs were gaining on him again.

a What does 'there was no doubt as to which way the vote would go' suggest about the situation the animals are now in and the mood of the extract?

b What is the significance of Napoleon's 'peculiar' and 'sidelong' look and the fact that he makes a sound that 'no one had ever heard him utter before'?

c Which pieces of language tell us about the appearance and actions of the dogs? Why is the use of this language significant?

d How do you think Orwell wants us to respond when we are told that 'Suddenly he slipped and it seemed certain that they had him'?

By ten o'clock, when the shops were closed, the by-street was very solitary and, in spite of the low growl of London from all round, very silent. Small sounds carried far; domestic sounds out of the houses were clearly audible on either side of the roadway; and the rumour of the approach of any passenger preceded him by a long time. Mr Utterson had been some minutes at his post, when he was aware of an odd, light footstep drawing near. In the course of his nightly patrols, he had long grown accustomed to the quaint effect with which the footfalls of a single person, while he is still a great way off, suddenly spring out distinct from the vast hum and clatter of the city. Yet his attention had never before been so sharply and decisively arrested; and it was with a strong, superstitious prevision of success that he withdrew into the entry of the court.

a What is the effect of the phrase 'the low growl of London'? What does it add to this extract?

b Sounds are described in great detail in this extract. What is the effect on the reader? Give examples to support your answer.

c What does the phrase 'the rumour of the approach of any passenger' add to the atmosphere of this extract?

d What impression might we get of Hyde from the description of 'an odd, light footstep drawing near'?

Activity 3

25 MINS

1 **Part (d)** of the examination question may ask you to explore the significance of a character, relationship, event, idea, theme or setting in a different extract from the text. You will choose the extract yourself.

a Read the question below relating to the text you have studied. List two extracts in the text which you could use in response to the question.

Animal Farm

Explore the significance of power in **one other** part of *Animal Farm*.
Use examples of the writer's language to support your answer.   (12 marks)

Dr Jekyll and Mr Hyde

Explore the importance of the setting in **one other** part of the novel.
Use examples of the writer's language to support your answer.   (12 marks)

Extracts (with brief description)

1. _____

2. _____

b Choose one of the extracts you have identified and list three examples of language that you can write about and note down what they tell you about the significance of the character, relationship, theme or setting.

Examples of language

1. _____

_____

2. _____

_____

3. _____

_____

2   The extracts on pages 88–89 also explore the themes of trust (*Animal Farm*) and tension (*Dr Jekyll and Mr Hyde*). Read the question below, which is part (d) of a sample examination question, relating to the novel you have studied. Choose an extract from the text and write two paragraphs in response to the question.

Animal Farm

Explore the importance of trust in the society of *Animal Farm* in **one other** part of the novel.
Use examples of the writer's language to support your answer.   (12 marks)

Dr Jekyll and Mr Hyde

Explore the significance of tension in **one other** part of the novel.
Use examples of the writer's language to support your answer.   (12 marks)

13 MINS

In this activity you will assess a student's work.

1   Re-read the extract in Activity 2 on pages 88–89 and then read the sample part (c) examination question and student's answer below.

Animal Farm

> Explore the significance of power in this extract. Use evidence from this extract to support your answer.   (10 marks)

In this extract, we can clearly see Napoleon abusing his power when he sets the dogs on Snowball before the animals have a chance to vote. However, his power is revealed in other ways too. We are told that there was 'no doubt as to which way the vote would go' which shows that the animals are more or less under Napoleon's control, suggesting that they are compliant and easily led by him. Napoleon now has his own personal army of dogs, who wear a uniform of 'brass-studded collars'. The uniform is a symbol of Napoleon's power, which is designed to intimidate the other animals. Napoleon is clearly taking on human characteristics, and this is shown by the fact that he has trained the dogs for his own purposes. He utters a 'high-pitched whimper' to call the dogs, which is similar to a human whistling to call dogs.

Dr Jekyll and Mr Hyde

> Explore the importance of the setting in this extract. Use evidence from the extract to support your answer.   (10 marks)

The writer uses sound to build up a picture in the reader's mind of the setting and create a tense atmosphere. The place where Utterson is waiting is described as 'very silent' yet the sounds he can hear are described in detail, for example 'the domestic sounds out of the houses'. This emphasises how alert Utterson is and how carefully he is listening, which builds suspense. The way the sounds are described also builds a sense of mystery, tension and excitement. The writer describes the 'low growl of London' which makes the city seem threatening and mysterious, like a wild animal or a monster. This also mirrors the monstrous nature of Hyde who is at large in the city. We hear Hyde before we see him, and even the sound of his footsteps is intriguing. They are 'odd' but also 'light', which may indicate that Hyde is trying to remain hidden, as if he is creeping up on Utterson.

2   Using the Higher Tier mark scheme for part (c) of an examination question, decide which band you think the student's answer would achieve and give your reasons.

Band	Description
3	• Sustained reference to context supported by relevant textual reference • Explanation of significance of theme in the extract shows thorough understanding
4	• Pertinent reference to context supported by relevant textual reference • Explanation of significance of theme in the extract shows assured understanding
5	• Convincing reference to context supported by sustained relevant textual reference • Explanation of significance of theme in the extract shows perceptive understanding

The student would obtain a Band _____ because _____

_____

ResultsPlus
Build your skills

Fill in the RAG table below to see how your confidence has improved in the following areas:

	R	A	G
I have a good understanding of the key themes within the text and can explain their significance	○	○	○
I can explain how the writer uses language to present a theme within an extract	○	○	○
I can select relevant examples from the text to support my points	○	○	○

4 Responding to an essay question

I need to:

- respond to the character, relationship, theme, event, idea or setting asked for in the question
- select appropriate details from the text to support my ideas
- evaluate these details from the text.

This lesson and Lesson 5 will help you to practise answering the single essay question you will be given for Section B of the examination. This question will ask you about a character, relationship, event, theme, idea or setting within the text you have studied. You will need to make reference to how the context of the text you have studied is relevant to the character, relationship, event, theme, idea or setting that you are writing about. This will be covered in Lesson 5.

ResultsPlus
Build your skills

Fill in the RAG table below to show how confident you are in the following areas:

	R	A	G
I can comment on the significance of the character, relationship, theme, event, idea or setting in a critical and imaginative way	○	○	○
I can select and evaluate appropriate details from the text to support my ideas	○	○	○
I can explain how language, structure and form contribute to a writer's presentation of a character, relationship, idea, theme, event or setting	○	○	○

Activity 1

This activity will help to remind you about some of the ideas on character, relationships and themes within the text you have studied.

15 MINS

1 Look at the table relating to your chosen text below. Match the statements to the character they refer to choosing from the options in the box.

Of Mice and Men

Lennie	George	Crooks	Candy	Curley's wife

✎	Character	Statement
		...soon realises that he can't be part of the dream.
		...has an unrealistic, glamorous dream.
		...realises that without the dream he will be miserable in old age.
		...uses the dream as a form of control.
		...completely believes in his dream.

To Kill a Mockingbird

Atticus   Scout   Aunt Alexandra

	Character	Statement
		...is old-fashioned.
		...does not treat Calpurnia as one of the family.
		...learns about racism and how to oppose it.
		...learns not to be prejudiced against Boo Radley.
		...helps the children learn right from wrong.
		...defends Tom because it is the right thing to do, even though it makes him unpopular.
		...discusses difficult issues with the children.

2 Below are some examples of the stems of the type of questions you may be asked in Section B of the examination, but with some words missing. Complete the questions by filling in the blanks with different key characters, relationships, events, themes, ideas or settings. There will be many possible options – try and come up with as many as you can. You will need to use a separate sheet of paper.

In what ways is the theme of _____ explored within the novel?

In what ways is the character of _____ important in the novel?

Why is the relationship between _____ and _____ significant in the novel?

Explore the significance of the setting of _____ in the novel.

Explore how the event of _____ affects different characters in the novel.

3 Now identify any of the questions you have created which you think you might find hard to answer. Make a note of them, so that you can come back to them in your revision later on.

Activity 2

1 Read the extract from your chosen text below along with the sample examination question. Imagine that you have selected the highlighted details to help you answer the essay question. What would you say about each of the highlighted phrases? Annotate the extract to show your ideas.

Of Mice and Men, Section 1, pages 14–15

Explore the significance of loneliness in the novel.

You must consider the context of the novel.

Use evidence to support your answer.   (40 marks)

George's voice became deeper. He repeated his words rhythmically as though he had said them many times before. 'Guys like us, that work on ranches, are the loneliest guys in the world. They got no family. They don't belong no place. They come to a ranch an' work up a stake and then they go inta town and blow their stake, and the first thing you know they're poundin' their tail on some other ranch. They ain't got nothing to look ahead to.'

Lennie was delighted. 'That's it – that's it. Now tell how it is with us.'

George went on. 'With us it ain't like that. We got a future. We got somebody to talk to that gives a damn about us. We don't have to sit in no bar room blowin' in our jack jus' because we got no place else to go. If them other guys gets in jail they can rot for all anybody gives a damn. But not us.'

Lennie broke in. *'But not us! An' why? Because … .because I got you to look after me, and you got me to look after you, and that's why.'* He laughed delightedly. 'Go on now, George!'

'You got it by heart. You can do it yourself.'

'No, you. I forget some a' the things. Tell about how it's gonna be.'

To Kill a Mockingbird, Chapter 9, pages 80–81

Explore the presentation of Finch family life.

You must consider the context of the novel.

Use evidence to support your answer. (40 marks)

Atticus had promised me he would wear me out if he ever heard of me fighting any more; I was far too old and too big for such childish things, and the sooner I learned to hold in, the better off everybody would be. I soon forgot.

Cecil Jacobs made me forget. He had announced in the schoolyard the day before that Scout Finch's daddy defended niggers. I denied it, but told Jem.

'What'd he mean sayin' that?' I asked.

'Nothing,' Jem said. 'Ask Atticus, he'll tell you.'

'Do you defend niggers, Atticus?' I asked him that evening.

'Of course I do. Don't say nigger, Scout. That's common.'

''s what everybody at school says.'

'From now on it'll be everybody less one –'

You will always need to make reference to more than one extract from your chosen text in response to the essay question. You will need to be able to quickly identify suitable extracts within your examination, using your knowledge of the text. This will help you to plan your response before you start to write.

2 Find at least two further extracts within your text which would be relevant when answering the exam question above. For *Of Mice and Men*, you might want to think about other characters who might be lonely (e.g. Curley's wife); for *To Kill a Mockingbird*, you might want to think about events that tell you something about the family's behaviour, e.g. Atticus' conflict with Aunt Alexandra about how to raise children.

Extract 1 _____

_____

Extract 2 _____

_____

Activity 3

25 MINS

This activity will help you continue to practise your skills in planning your response to the Section B essay question. You will not only need to identify the extracts from the text to use but also the points you will make within your response.

1 Read the question below. Think carefully about how you want to answer the question. List four main points that you will make in your essay.

Of Mice and Men

> Explain the importance of George and Lennie's friendship in the novel.
>
> (40 marks)

To Kill a Mockingbird

> Explore how important the Tom Robinson case is to Atticus. (40 marks)

Point 1: _____

_____

Point 2: _____

_____

Point 3: _____

_____

Point 4: _____

_____

2 Now note down which extracts from your text you could use as an example to back up your points. Identify specific pieces of evidence within the extract you will use where possible and explain why these are relevant.

The first extract I will comment on is _____

because _____

_____

The second extract I will comment on is _____

because _____

_____

The third extract I will comment on is _____

because _____

_____

3 Look back at one of the questions you created in Activity 1 Question 3 and use it to repeat the process above. Decide on the main points you will make in your essay, and then identify the extracts from the text you will use to support these points.

_____

_____

_____

_____

_____

_____

10 MINS

1 Read the extract below from a sample response to the question you looked at in Activity 3. Look at the Higher Tier mark scheme for AO1. Which band do you think each answer would achieve? Explain your reasons.

Of Mice and Men

George and Lennie are together because they are different to other people. They want to spend the rest of their lives together. George does get angry with Lennie though. For example, at the beginning of the novel George shouts 'Give it here!' when Lennie has a dead mouse in his pocket. Lennie gives in. It says Lennie's hand 'slowly obeyed.' George explains to Slim that Lennie had been brought up by his Aunt Clara and Lennie just used to work with George. When Aunt Clara died Lennie and George just stuck together. But it was strange for people to stick together on ranches in those days. George and Lennie share a dream and this makes them different and this is why they stay together.

To Kill a Mockingbird

When Atticus takes on the case of Tom Robinson, he makes it clear that he will try his hardest to defend him. This angers many people in Maycomb, who don't think anyone should defend Tom as he is black. As a result, Atticus and his family go through some hard times. However, Atticus is not racist and thinks Tom should get a fair trial, so he carries on with the case anyway. This affects his family. Scout is bullied at school by Cecil Jacobs and later on Bob Ewell tries to attack her and Jem in revenge.

Band	Description
3	• Sustained responses to text supported by relevant textual reference • Selection and evaluation of textual detail show thorough understanding of theme/ideas
4	• Pertinent responses to text supported by relevant textual reference • Selection and evaluation of textual detail show assured understanding of theme/ideas
5	• Convincing responses to text supported by sustained relevant textual reference • Selection and evaluation of textual detail show perceptive understanding of theme/ideas

The student would obtain a Band _____ because _____

_____

_____

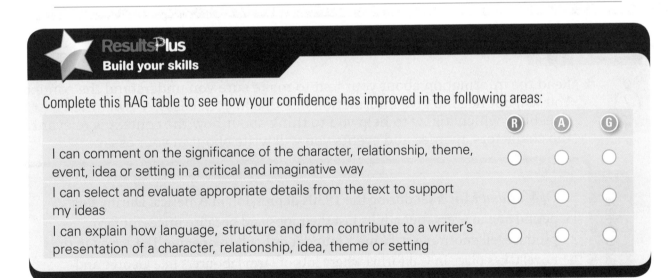

ResultsPlus
Build your skills

Complete this RAG table to see how your confidence has improved in the following areas:

	R	A	G
I can comment on the significance of the character, relationship, theme, event, idea or setting in a critical and imaginative way	○	○	○
I can select and evaluate appropriate details from the text to support my ideas	○	○	○
I can explain how language, structure and form contribute to a writer's presentation of a character, relationship, idea, theme or setting	○	○	○

Remember that your final response in the examination will not only be marked against the mark scheme above but also the mark scheme that is shown on page 109 (AO4). This means you will also be assessed on how you consider the context of the text within your response on a character, relationship, event, theme, idea or setting, and Lesson 5 will help you to prepare for this. You will also be assessed on your use of spelling, punctuation and grammar within your response, and Lesson 6 will help you to prepare for this.

5 Responding to the context of the text

I need to:

- **show an awareness of the importance of the context of the text**
- **explain the importance of the character, relationship, event, idea, theme or setting**
- **structure my sentences and spell and punctuate accurately.**

This lesson will continue to help you prepare for the essay question you will tackle in Section B of the English Literature Unit 1 examination. You will be writing about a character, relationship, event, theme, idea or setting, and you will need to show some understanding of the context of your text within your response, e.g. by explaining why Curley's wife behaves as she does on the ranch, or by giving some suggestions as to why Tom Robinson was accused of the rape of Mayella Ewell. You should not write detailed or extensive historical, social or cultural information within your essay.

ResultsPlus
Build your skills

Fill in the RAG table below to show how confident you are in the following areas:

	R	A	G
I can make reference to the text's context, supported by references to the text	◯	◯	◯
I can explain important themes and ideas, and how these relate to the context	◯	◯	◯
I can structure my sentences so the meaning is clear, use a full range of punctuation and spell accurately	◯	◯	◯

Activity 1

15 MINS

1   Read the information about your text to make sure you understand the context. You will not need to give information like this in your essay. Answer the questions which follow to help you to think about how the context is relevant to the characters, themes and events you will write about in your essay.

Of Mice and Men

Of Mice and Men is set during the 1930s depression in America. During this period one in every four adults lost their jobs and because prices for farm produce fell enormously, farmers found it difficult to operate. The action in the novel takes place in California where lots of farm labourers like George and Lennie travelled alone from farm to farm looking for work. Jobs often lasted for only a short time and then the workers had to move on to look for more work. Because they often travelled alone there were very few friendships.

a   In the depression, farm prices fell. Wages also fell and there was no job security. How does this affect the characters in *Of Mice and Men*?

_____

_____

b Most farm jobs only lasted for a short time on the ranches. How does this affect the characters in the novel?

c In the 1930s it was difficult for women to be independent. How is this shown in the novel?

To Kill a Mockingbird

To Kill a Mockingbird is set during the 1930s in America. Because of the depression many families, both whites and African Americans, were poor. The novel is set in Alabama and focuses on the racism of a small town. Although slavery was abolished in 1865, African Americans were still treated very badly at this time. In the South, there were laws which said that African Americans and white people could not mix. There were separate schools, restaurants and even water fountains. Although the law said that all Americans were equal, in practice, juries almost always believed white people over African Americans.

a The depression of the 1930s meant that a lot of people were very poor. Who is poor in the novel? How does Harper Lee show this?

b African Americans were supposed to be 'separate but equal' to white people in the southern states of the US. Are the African American characters treated in an 'equal' way in the novel? Explain your answer.

c Bob Ewell is one of the most racist characters in the book. Why do you think this is?

Activity 2

15 MINS

1 Look at the sample examination question relevant to the text you have studied on page 106. Then look at the short extract below and answer the questions to help you start thinking about how to respond to the sample examination question. Remember that you will not be given an extract or questions like this in the examination.

Of Mice and Men, Section 2, page 34

Both men glanced up for the rectangle of sunshine in the doorway was cut off. A girl was standing there looking in. She had full, rouged lips and wide-spaced eyes, heavily made up. Her fingernails were red. Her hair hung in little rolled clusters, like sausages. She wore a cotton house dress and red mules, on the insteps of which were little bouquets of red ostrich feathers. 'I'm lookin' for Curley,' she said. Her voice had a nasal, brittle quality.

George looked away from her and then back. 'He was in here a minute ago, but he went.'

'Oh!' She put her hands behind her back and leaned against the door frame so that her body was thrown forward. 'You're the new fellas that just come, ain't ya?'

'Yeah.'

Lennie's eyes moved down over her body, and though she did not seem to be looking at Lennie, she bridled a little. She looked at her fingernails. 'Sometimes Curley's in here,' she explained.

a Why might the ranchers feel that Curley's wife is 'a tart'?

_____

_____

b What is the role of Curley's wife on the ranch? Were there many women on ranches in 1930s America?

_____

_____

c How do the men respond to Curley's wife's behaviour?

_____

_____

d Why does Curley's wife flirt with the men?

_____

_____

To Kill a Mockingbird Chapter 17, pages 178–179

'What time was it, Mr Ewell?'

'Just 'fore sundown. Well, I was sayin' Mayella was screamin' fit to beat Jesus –' another glance from the bench silenced Mr Ewell.

'Yes? She was screaming?' said Mr Gilmer.

Mr Ewell looked confusedly at the judge. 'Well, Mayella was raisin' this holy racket so I dropped m'load and run as fast as I could but I run into th'fence, but when I got distangled I run up to th'window and I seen –' Mr Ewell's face grew scarlet. He stood and pointed his finger at Tom Robinson. '– I seen that black nigger yonder ruttin' on my Mayella!'

So serene was Judge Taylor's court, that he had few occasions to use his gavel, but he hammered fully five minutes. Atticus was on his feet at the bench saying something to him, Mr Heck Tate as first officer of the county stood in the middle aisle quelling the packed courtroom. Behind us, there was an angry muffled groan from the coloured people.

Reverend Sykes leaned across Dill and me, pulling at Jem's elbow. 'Mr Jem,' he said, 'you better take Miss Jean Louise home. Mr Jem, you hear me?'

a How does Bob Ewell present himself in court? Why?

_____

_____

b What kind of language does Bob Ewell use? How do the people in court react?

_____

_____

c How does Bob Ewell's language compare with that used by Tom Robinson?

_____

_____

d Why do the jury believe Bob Ewell over Tom Robinson?

_____

_____

Activity 3

20 MINS

1 Read the sample examination question below for your text. Write a short plan for your answer, deciding on the points you will make and the extracts from your text which you will use. You may want to use the extract that you looked at in Activity 2 as one of the extracts you discuss.

Of Mice and Men

In what ways is the character of Curley's wife significant in the novel?

You must consider the context of the novel.

Use evidence to support your answer.

(40 marks)

To Kill a Mockingbird

In what ways are Bob and Mayella Ewell significant in the novel?

You must consider the context of the novel.

Use evidence to support your answer.

(40 marks)

_____

_____

_____

_____

_____

_____

_____

_____

_____

2 Now write at least two paragraphs in response to the sample examination question. Remember that you need to make reference to the context of your text wherever this is appropriate to support your points in order to gain good marks. Remember that your writing will also be assessed for spelling, punctuation and grammar, so pay close attention to this when writing your response. Lesson 6 will help you to prepare for this assessment.

3 Now check over your response to ensure you have done the following:

- given evidence from the text to support your answer
- made reference to the context of the novel wherever this is appropriate to explore the character, relationship, event, theme, idea or setting you are writing about
- used correct spelling, punctuation and grammar in your writing.

10 MINS

1 Read the extract taken from a student's response to the sample examination question in Activity 3, and at the Higher Tier mark scheme. This mark scheme will be used to assess your essay in the examination, along with the mark scheme in Lesson 4, page 101. Decide which band you think the student answer would achieve and explain your reasons. Remember that there are also up to 6 additional marks available for spelling, punctuation and grammar, so familiarise yourself with the additional mark scheme on page 121 and apply it to these answers.

Of Mice and Men

Curley's wife is an extremely significant person on the ranch. First of all, through her we see the way men responded to women in 1930s America. If she represents the position of women in 1930s American society then we can see that women suffered from unfulfilled dreams. As a teenager Curley's wife was seduced by the glamorous life of Hollywood, only a few miles away from Soledad, in Los Angeles. In an attempt to escape the control of her mother she married Curley but then discovered that this was not the answer to her dreams. Curley was extremely possessive and treated his wife with little respect. The fact that he told the ranch workers that he was keeping one of his hands 'soft for his wife' coupled with the fact that she is only ever known as 'Curley's wife' suggests that she is an object.

To Kill a Mockingbird

Harper Lee uses the characters of Bob and Mayella Ewell and their behaviour to highlight just how deeply racist and unjust Maycomb society is. Throughout the novel, the reader is invited to contrast Bob Ewell with the black community in Maycomb in order to show the extent of the racism in the society. Bob is an abusive, violent man who does not care for his children and uses bad language, yet in Maycomb, he is still considered to be more trustworthy than any black person, however good. In court, Bob Ewell uses graphic language and says that 'I seen that black nigger yonder ruttin' on my Mayella!' This language is considered so shocking that Reverend Sykes wants the children to leave the courtroom. In contrast, Tom Robinson does not want to repeat the language Bob Ewell used when he entered the house because he says it's 'not fittin' for these folks' n chillun to hear'. However polite and considerate Tom is, the jury will always believe Bob Ewell because he is white.

Band	Description
3	• Sustained reference to context supported by relevant textual reference • Explanation of importance of theme/idea shows thorough understanding • Sentences are appropriately structured, with sustained control of expression and meaning with thorough control of the full range of punctuation devices Spelling is almost always accurate, with occasional errors
4	• Pertinent reference to context supported by relevant textual reference • Explanation of importance of theme/idea shows assured understanding • Sentences are purposefully structured, with assured control of expression and meaning with assured control of the full range of punctuation devices Spelling is almost always accurate, with minimal errors
5	• Convincing reference to context supported by sustained relevant textual reference • Explanation of importance of theme/idea shows perceptive understanding • Sentences are convincingly structured, with sophisticated control of expression and meaning with precise control of the full range of punctuation devices. Spelling is consistently accurate

The student's answer would obtain a Band _____ because _____

_____

_____

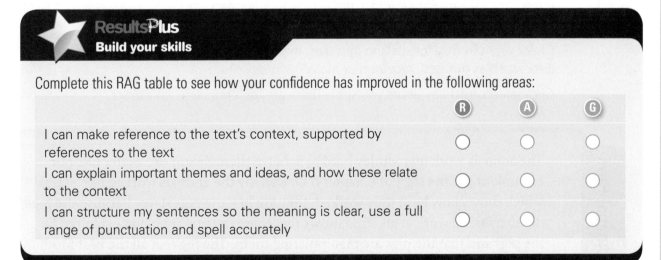

ResultsPlus
Build your skills

Complete this RAG table to see how your confidence has improved in the following areas:

	R	A	G
I can make reference to the text's context, supported by references to the text	○	○	○
I can explain important themes and ideas, and how these relate to the context	○	○	○
I can structure my sentences so the meaning is clear, use a full range of punctuation and spell accurately	○	○	○

6 Spelling, punctuation and grammar

I need to:

• **check that my spelling and punctuation are accurate**

• **make sure my writing is grammatically correct and my ideas are clearly expressed**

• **accurately use a range of key specialist vocabulary where required.**

This lesson will help you improve the spelling, punctuation and grammar in your answers to Unit 1 Section A part (d) and Unit 1 Section B of the English Literature exam. You will be awarded up to 3 additional marks for Section A part (d) and up to 6 additional marks for Section B based on how well you have used spelling, punctuation and grammar in your answers.

Expressing your ideas clearly and accurately shows how clearly you understand the texts you have studied. It may be worth just 5% of the overall marks available, but that could make the difference between the grade you want to achieve and the one below it.

ResultsPlus
Build your skills

Fill in the RAG table below to show how confident you are in the following areas:

	R	A	G
I can identify and correct my spelling errors	○	○	○
I can check that my punctuation is accurate	○	○	○
I can check my writing makes sense and is clearly expressed	○	○	○
I can accurately use a range of key specialist vocabulary	○	○	○

Activity 1

10 MINS

1 The following extracts are taken from students' responses to Section A part (d) for either *Animal Farm* or *Dr Jekyll and Mr Hyde*. Read through the extract relevant to the text you are studying. What kinds of mistakes can you find in it?

Check very carefully for spelling mistakes, missing or incorrect punctuation and grammatical errors such as misused, repeated or missing words.

Circle and correct any errors you spot. There are ten errors in each extract.

Animal Farm

> The animals work incredibley hard to acheive there dream of a better life. For example at the the start of Chapter 6 Orwell say the animals worked like 'slaves' which shows how hard they worked, they are like the pigs slaves because the pigs do no pyhsical work at all. This shows that there dreams are being exploited by the pigs and that the pigs are manipulating them. The pigs eat all the best food, drink alcahol, sleep in beds and treet the other animals no better than the humans used to.

Dr Jekyll and Mr Hyde

Stevenson creates a sense of mystery from the very begining of the story, he describes a busy streets "freshly painted shutters" and it's "cleanliness". He then contrasts this with a "sinister" building which seems to have no windows only a door without a knocker of a bell. This then leads onto Enfields story of the sinister man who beat the small girl. Straight away Stevenson creats a mystery in the setting and the charcters of his story. The reader is left wondering why this 'sinister' windowless building is so diffrent to the others and what secrets it holds, and why someone would be so cruel and violent to beat a vunerable young girl.

The mark scheme below will be used to assess the spelling, punctuation and grammar of responses to Section A part (d) questions. Study it and decide what Level you would give the student answer you have just read, explaining your reasons.

Level	Marks	Description
0	0	Errors severely hinder the meaning of the response or candidates do not spell, punctuate or use the rules of grammar within the context of the demands of the question.
1	1	Candidates spell, punctuate and use the rules of grammar with reasonable accuracy in the context of the demands of the question. Any errors do not hinder meaning in the response. Where required, they use a limited range of specialist terms appropriately.
2	2	Candidates spell, punctuate and use the rules of grammar with considerable accuracy and general control of meaning in the context of the demands of the question. Where required, they use a good range of specialist terms with facility.
3	3	Candidates spell, punctuate and use the rules of grammar with consistent accuracy and effective control of meaning in the context of the demands of the question. Where required, they use a wide range of specialist terms adeptly and with precision.

I would award the student a Level _____ because _____

_____

_____

_____

Activity 2

10 MINS

There are some spelling and grammar mistakes which occur again and again in students' exam responses.

> Students often use *would of*, *should of* or *could of* when they should use *would have*, *should have* or *could have*. For example:
>
> > - The pigs in Animal Farm could of treated the other animals more fairly. ✗
> > - This suggests that Dr Jekyll should of considered the consequences before he experimented on himself. ✗

> Students sometimes use *our* when they should use *are*. For example:
>
> > - Boxer and Mollie our both horses but they our very different. ✗

> It is easy to confuse *their*, *there* and *they're*:
> - *Their* means belonging to them.
> - *There* is used to describe the position of something, as in *it's over there,* and in the phrases *there is* or *there are*.
> - *They're* is short for *they are*.
>
> Students often make the wrong choice. For example:
>
> > - Jekyll recognises their is evil within him. ✗
> > - The animals must live there lives according to the seven commandments. ✗

> Students sometimes mix up *effect* and *affect*. *Affect* is a verb. *Effect* is usually used as a noun. So, for example, the reader can be <u>affected</u> by the language the writer uses. But the language can have an <u>effect</u> on the reader. If the word has got *an* or *the* in front of it, it's a noun, so it's spelt *effect*.

Write at least five sentences about your set text for Section A: Literary Heritage. In each sentence, use at least one of the words and phrases listed above which students often get wrong. Then check your sentences carefully to make sure you are not making any mistakes.

1   A sentence using *their*:

_____

_____

2   A sentence using *there*:

_____

_____

3   A sentence using *they're*:

_____

_____

4   A sentence using *are* not *our*:

_____

_____

5   A sentence using *would/should/could have*:

_____

_____

Activity 3

When you write a formal essay or exam response, it is important that you use formal standard English to express your ideas. The following students have used informal language in their exam answers to Section B: Different Cultures and Traditions. Read the sentences taken from their answers related to the text you have studied and rewrite each sentence using formal standard English.

Of Mice and Men

1   George gets well angry with Lennie at loads of different times in the novel.

_____

2   IMO Curley is a mean bloke who treats his wife like dirt.

_____

3   Curley is always up for a fight cos he's small and wants to prove himself.

_____

4   After a bit, Lennie loses his rag and mashes Curley's hand.

_____

To Kill A Mockingbird

1   Scout's behaviour is not always the best.

_____

2   Scout smacks her cousin cos he disses her dad.

_____

3   BTW Atticus is quite a harsh dad and sometimes has a go at Scout.

_____

4   Scout's heart is in the right place and she usually does the right thing.

_____

Activity 4

10 MINS

In your exam answers, you might use some or all of the specialist key terms below. Each one is spelt incorrectly.

- aliteration
- similie
- metaphore
- personnification
- repitition
- onomatapeioa
- narrater
- charactor
- veiwpoint

It is important that you spell them correctly and use them accurately.

Check the correct spelling of each word using a dictionary, and write it next to the correct definition:

Specialist Key Term	Definition
	Two or more words, near or next to each other, beginning with the same letter or sound, e.g. 'snapped swiftly shut'
	A word whose sound imitates its meaning, e.g. 'crash'
	A comparison of two different things, using *like* or *as*
	A <u>direct</u> comparison of two different things, without the use of *like* or *as*
	A kind of metaphor, describing a non-human object as if it were a person
	One of the people represented in a story or play
	A word or phrase repeated for effect
	The author's opinion or attitude expressed in a piece of writing
	The person in whose 'voice' a story is told

Activity 5

5 MINS

Accurate punctuation makes your writing easy to read and understand. Incorrect or missing punctuation could mean that your meaning is lost and you won't be able to demonstrate how well you know and understand your set text.

Getting the full stops in the right place is the first thing to check, along with making sure you are not using a comma when you should use a full stop. Look at the extract from the relevant student response below, in answer to the Section B: Different Cultures and Traditions exam question. Add full stops and capital letters where they are needed.

Of Mice and Men

George and Lennie are not the only characters with dreams in the novel, Curley's wife once had dreams of being a film star, now she dreams of escaping her loveless marriage like George and Lennie Crooks and Candy also dream of a place of their own

To Kill A Mockingbird

The people of Maycomb county have very fixed attitudes, this includes their attitudes to each other and what they consider acceptable behaviour, perhaps their most telling attitudes are to the Radley family and the black population of the town

Activity 6

5 MINS

One of the most common punctuation errors is the incorrect use of the apostrophe or missing it out altogether. There are two reasons to use an apostrophe:

When you shorten or abbreviate words:

cannot → can't

do not → don't

Abbreviations such as *don't* and *can't* are too informal for an exam answer. Use the full, unabbreviated version in your writing.

To show possession or belonging:

| Curley's wife | Scout's brother |

Note that if the word to which you are adding the apostrophe ends in 's' you can either add the extra 's' or miss it out:

| Crooks's room | Atticus's children |

or

| Crooks' room | Atticus' children |

Of Mice and Men

The dress belonging to the wife of Curley	Curley's wife's dress
The dog belonging to Candy	
The glove belonging to Curley	
The son of the Boss	
The books belonging to Crooks	

To Kill A Mockingbird

The imprisonment of Tom Robinson	Tom Robinson's imprisonment
The voice belonging to Atticus	
The novel written by Harper Lee	
The childhood of Scout	
The attitudes of the people of Maycomb	

Activity 7

10 MINS

There is more to accurate punctuation than getting your full stops and apostrophes in the right place. You can use advanced punctuation to develop your ideas and express them fully.

For example, you could use semi-colons to link two connected ideas instead of using a connective.

Of Mice and Men

You could write:

> Crooks is not allowed in the bunkhouse and lives in enforced isolation in the barn.

...or you could write:

> Crooks is not allowed in the bunkhouse; he lives in enforced isolation in the barn.

To Kill A Mockingbird

You could write:

> Scout is fiercely proud and has a quick temper so she will not allow an insult to her father to go unpunished.

...or you could write:

> Scout is fiercely proud and has a quick temper; she will not allow an insult to her father to go unpunished.

1 Write three sentences about your set text for Section B, using a **connective** or **joining word** to link two ideas in each one.

a _____

_____

_____

b _____

_____

_____

c _____

_____

_____

2 Rewrite the same three sentences, **replacing** the connective with a **semi-colon**.

a _____

_____

_____

b _____

_____

_____

c _____

_____

_____

10 MINS

1 The extracts below are from student responses to Unit 1 Section B of the English Literature exam. Read the response related to the text you have studied and look at the mark scheme for spelling, punctuation and grammar opposite. Which Level do you think the answer would achieve? Explain your reasons.

Of Mice and Men

Task:

Why is the treatment that Crooks receives from other characters important in the novel?

You **must** consider the context of the novel in your answer.

Use **evidence** to support your answer.

Curleys wife has been dissapointed in her own dreams and is as lonley and isolated as Crooks. Howver she is very ready to crush his spirit and his dreems when she tells him "I could get you strung up on a tree so easy". Reminded of his roll in society, Crooks "reduced himself to nothing". The word "nothing" sugests he is seen as worthless and that he trys to make himslef invisible so that poeple wont pick on him, this shows that even when poeple are in very simular situations they do not have any sumpathy for each other.

To Kill a Mockingbird

Task:

What does the reader learn from Scout's account of life in Maycomb County?

You **must** consider the context of the novel in your answer.

Use **evidence** to support your answer.

Although there are some people in Maycomb who support Atticus's decision to defend Tom Robinson, the verdict in his trail makes the reader realise how prejudiced most of the townspeople are: 'Guilty... guilty... guilty... guilty...' Lee uses repitition to hammer home the verdict, and compares each word to a 'separate stab' between Jem's shoulder blades. This shows the reader how upset Jem is and how unfair he feels the verdict is. Atticus seems to know that this would happen. He says 'They've done it before and they did it tonight and they'll do it again". This suggests that like everything else in Maycomb people's racist attitudes will not change.

Level	Marks	Description
0	0	Errors severely hinder the meaning of the response or candidates do not spell, punctuate or use the rules of grammar within the context of the demands of the question.
1	1-2	Candidates spell, punctuate and use the rules of grammar with reasonable accuracy in the context of the demands of the question. Any errors do not hinder meaning in the response. Where required, they use a limited range of specialist terms appropriately.
2	3-4	Candidates spell, punctuate and use the rules of grammar with considerable accuracy and general control of meaning in the context of the demands of the question. Where required, they use a good range of specialist terms with facility.
3	5-6	Candidates spell, punctuate and use the rules of grammar with consistent accuracy and effective control of meaning in the context of the demands of the question. Where required, they use a wide range of specialist terms adeptly and with precision.

I would award the student a Level _____ because _____

_____

_____

2   Look very carefully at the relevant student response on page 120. Correct all the spelling, punctuation and grammar mistakes you identify.

3   Now look carefully at just one paragraph of your own writing from another section of this workbook. Check very carefully for spelling mistakes, missing or incorrect punctuation or grammatical errors such as misused, repeated or missing words.

4   Make a list of the kinds of errors you make.

ResultsPlus
Build your skills

Fill in the RAG table below to show how your confidence has improved in the following areas:

	R	A	G
I can identify and correct my spelling errors	○	○	○
I can check that my punctuation is accurate	○	○	○
I can check my writing makes sense and is clearly expressed	○	○	○
I can accurately use a range of key specialist vocabulary	○	○	○

1 Writing about an unseen poem

I need to:

- **show that I understand what the poem is about**
- **show that I understand the writer's ideas**
- **explain how the writer uses structure, language and form to present their ideas**
- **give well-chosen examples from the poem to support my points.**

This lesson will help you to practise answering Section A of the examination for Unit 2 Understanding Poetry.

In Section A you will need to read a poem you have not seen before and explain how the writer uses language, form and structure to present an idea, a theme, or a setting within the poem. You should support your explanation with a few examples from the poem that are really relevant.

ResultsPlus
Build your skills

Fill in the RAG table below to show how confident you are in the following areas:

	R	A	G
I can recognise a range of poetic devices	○	○	○
I can comment on particular vocabulary	○	○	○
I can comment on the way a poem is organised	○	○	○
I can explain how the writer uses poetic devices, vocabulary and structure to present their ideas	○	○	○

Activity 1

10 MINS

1 Read the poem 'In Mrs Tilscher's Class' and annotate it, identifying the key ideas and/or feelings of the poem.

> **In Mrs Tilscher's Class**
>
> You could travel up the Blue Nile
> with your finger, tracing the route
> while Mrs Tilscher chanted the scenery.
> Tana. Ethiopia. Khartoum. Aswân.
> That for an hour, then a skittle of milk
> and the chalky Pyramids rubbed into dust.
> A window opened with a long pole.
> The laugh of a bell swung by a running child.
>
> This was better than home. Enthralling books.
> The classroom glowed like a sweet shop.
> Sugar paper. Coloured shapes. Brady and Hindley
> faded, like the faint, uneasy smudge of a mistake.
> Mrs Tilscher loved you. Some mornings, you found
> she'd left a good gold star by your name.
> The scent of a pencil slowly, carefully, shaved.
> A xylophone's nonsense heard from another form.

Over the Easter term, the inky tadpoles changed
from commas into exclamation marks. Three frogs
hopped in the playground, freed by a dunce,
followed by a line of kids, jumping and croaking
away from the lunch queue. A rough boy
told you how you were born. You kicked him, but stared
at your parents, appalled, when you got back home.

That feverish July, the air tasted of electricity.
A tangible alarm made you always untidy, hot,
Fractious under the heavy, sexy sky. You asked her
how you were born and Mrs Tilscher smiled,
then turned away. Reports were handed out.
You ran through the gates, impatient to be grown,
as the sky split open into a thunderstorm.

Carol Ann Duffy

2 Now fill in the following table to help you think about the language, structure and form of the poem and the effect of these.

The form of the poem	Answer with example	Importance in presenting ideas/feelings of poem
Who is speaking in the poem?		
Who or what is addressed?		
What can you say about the use of rhyme?		
What can you say about the poem's rhythm?		
How does the type of language and the tone used change throughout the poem?		

Activity 2

15 MINS

1 Read the short extracts taken from different poems below.

2 Find at least one example of each of the poetic devices/language features listed in the table opposite and write the examples you have found in the first white column. Then fill in the final column by commenting on how these support the idea, theme or setting presented in the extracts. One example has been completed for you.

I am the wind

I am the wisdom and the freedom,
I am the storm that tears and howls,
I am the whispering in the treetops,
I slide beneath you,
swirl around you,
stroke your hair,
and take your breath away.

Anon

Extract taken from http://1-poem.com/i_am_the_wind_personification_
exercise.htm, 1-poem.com, © *copyright Dr Silvia Hartmann, www.1-poem.com*

The Warm and the Cold

Freezing dusk is closing
        Like a slow trap of steel
On trees and roads and hills and all
        That can no longer feel.

Ted Hughes

The City

In the morning the city
Spreads its wings
Making a song
In stone that sings.

Langston Hughes

She walks in beauty

She walks in beauty, like the night
        Of cloudless climes and starry skies;
And all that's best of dark and bright
        Meet in her aspect and her eyes…

Lord Byron (George Gorden)

Ode to the West Wind

O wild West Wind, thou breath of Autumn's being

Percy Bysshe Shelley

Poetic devices/language features	Example(s)	How ideas/feelings are presented
a Personification	O wild West Wind, thou breath of Autumn's being	This helps to show how overwhelming the wind is to the poet, with the capitalisation of 'West Wind' to make it seem like a person with a personality of its own. The use of the pronoun 'thou', means that he is addressing the wind directly. The adjective 'wild' also makes this phrase an example of alliteration and onomatopoeia.
b Simile		
c Alliteration		
d Metaphor		
e Use of adjectives		

When you read a new poem, it is helpful first to identify the main ideas, feeling or tone of the poem. Once you have done this, you can think about how the writer has used poetic devices, language and structure to get across their ideas or create the tone.

Activity 3

1 Read the poem below and identify the key ideas and tone.

THE DRIVING LESSON

"Gently, now slow down and stop, HALT!"
And the car jerks and bucks like a young colt,
And she grits her teeth and blinks back the tears,
Gripping the wheel like an axe, wanting to split
The tension, so that like snapped elastic,
There will be release and, for him, the sharp
Stinging pain of rebound.

But instead the mutters cease and
Pressing her foot on the clutch as if on his head,
The car lurches forward to a goal,
Like a young baby's first uncertain steps,
Gathering speed, shifting weight, staggering
Drunkenly, a hair's breadth from disaster,
Just missing obstacles.

And she hates him with unswerving passion.
The pebbly eyes and cynical stare
Break her down as she grinds up a gear.
And the clipped "I think we'll call it a day, dear,
So get out and I'll take over from here."
And a clear certainty tells her that soon
She will wrench off his hand-brake and run.

Jane Linstead

2 Complete the table opposite by finding as many examples as possible of each of the poetic devices/language features in the first column of the table and commenting on how they are used to present the poem's ideas, thoughts or feelings. You may wish to annotate the poem to help you. One example has been completed for you.

Poetic devices/ Language features	Example	How this is used to present the poem's ideas, thoughts or feelings
a Use of adjectives	Snapped elastic	The word shows how she imagines the tension that has built up suddenly breaking because it can go no further
b Simile		
c Use of verbs		
d Use of rhyme		

3 Now write a paragraph on a separate piece of paper in response to the following sample examination question, using the notes you made above as a guide.

> Explore how Jane Linstead presents the woman's experience of learning to drive.
>
> Use evidence from the poem to support your answer. (20 marks)

Remember that you will have to write your response to the examination question in full, clear sentences. Your response to the unseen poem question is also marked for 'Quality of Written Communication'. This means that you will get marked down if your spelling, grammar and punctuation are not accurate.

4 Read through your answer carefully, checking for meaning and correct spelling, grammar and punctuation.

Build better answers

1 Read the extract from the student response to the sample examination question in Activity 3. Highlight all the extracts from the poem on page 114 that the student has included in their response as evidence to support their points.

10 MINS

> In this poem the writer uses powerful imagery to create the sense that the learner driver is finding her lesson to be something of an ordeal. Right from the start, she feels that she is being criticised by the (male) instructor, who barks out his orders in an increasingly harsh way: he starts by saying 'Gently' and gets more aggressive, as is shown by the capital letters and exclamation mark for 'HALT!' You obtain a very clear picture of her desperate efforts to stay in control, although she feels like running away, as she 'grits her teeth' and 'blinks back the tears'. She grips the steering wheel 'like an axe', which suggests she holds on to it tightly. It also suggests that she would like it to be a weapon – she is clearly having violent thoughts towards the instructor. The idea that the tension has increased almost to breaking point is shown by the simile 'like snapped elastic', and this is made more effective because she imagines the elastic smacking into the instructor's face as it rebounds, reflecting the violence of her feelings.

2 Look at the Higher Tier mark scheme and remind yourself of the descriptions of each band. Decide in which of the bands you would put the student's answer. Fill in the blanks to explain your decision.

The students's answer is in Band _____ because _____

_____

_____

Band	Description
3	• Thorough understanding of the poem's content/ideas • Thorough explanation of how the writer uses language, structure and form to present the poem's content/ideas • Sustained relevant textual reference to support response • Appropriate organisation and sustained communication of ideas. Spelling, punctuation and grammar is almost always accurate, with occasional errors
4	• Assured understanding of the poem's content/ideas • Assured explanation of how the writer uses language, structure and form to present the poem's content/ideas • Pertinent references are made to the poem to support points • Pertinent relevant textual reference to support response • Purposeful organisation and assured communication of ideas. Spelling, punctuation and grammar is almost always accurate, with minimal errors
5	• Perceptive understanding of the poem's content/ideas • Perceptive explanation of how the writer uses language, structure and form to present the poem's content/ideas • Convincing relevant textual reference to support response • Convincing organisation and sophisticated communication of ideas. Spelling, punctuation and grammar is consistently accurate

ResultsPlus
Build your skills

Fill in the RAG table below to see how your confidence has improved in the following areas:

	R	A	G
I can recognise a range of poetic devices	○	○	○
I can comment on particular vocabulary	○	○	○
I can comment on the way a poem is organised	○	○	○
I can explain how the writer uses poetic devices, vocabulary and structure to present their ideas	○	○	○

2 Commenting on one anthology poem

I need to:
- explore the writer's attitudes, ideas and feelings in the poem
- explore how the writer uses language, structure and form to convey these ideas, thoughts and feelings
- use relevant examples from the poem to support my points.

This lesson will help you prepare for the Section B Anthology Poems section of your examination.

You **must** answer part (a).

- **Part (a)** will ask you to comment on the writer's thoughts or feelings in a poem from your anthology collection.

You should answer **either** part (b)(i) **or** part (b)(ii).

- **Part (b)(i)** will ask you to compare the writer's ideas in the poem from part (a) with another named poem from the anthology.

- **Part (b)(ii)** will ask you to compare the writer's ideas in the poem from part (a) with a poem of your choice from the anthology.

This lesson focuses on **part (a)** of the question. This will ask you to explore how the writer conveys their attitudes, ideas, thoughts or feelings using examples of language from the poem.

ResultsPlus
Build your skills

Fill in the RAG table below to show how confident you are in the following areas:

	R	A	G
I can recognise a range of poetic devices and comment on their effect	○	○	○
I can comment on the effect of particular vocabulary	○	○	○
I can comment on the effect of the structure and form of a poem	○	○	○
I can choose relevant examples from the poem to support my points	○	○	○

Activity 1

10 MINS

Part (a) of the examination question will ask you to write about the writer's ideas, thoughts or feelings in one of the poems you have studied in your chosen collection in the anthology. Before you go into the examination it is important to know what these key ideas, thoughts and feelings are and how they are presented using language.

1   Choose three poems from your anthology collection. Briefly summarise the main ideas, thoughts and feelings in each poem in the boxes opposite.

2   Writers can use language to present their ideas. For example, they may use simile and metaphor, personification, interesting vocabulary, alliteration, assonance, onomatopoeia, rhythm and rhyme. Choose three techniques the writer uses to present their ideas in each poem you have summarised. Record your ideas in the boxes opposite.

Poem 1

Ideas, thoughts and feelings in the poem:

Techniques used by the poet:

Poem 2

Ideas, thoughts and feelings in the poem:

Techniques used by the poet:

Poem 3

Ideas, thoughts and feelings in the poem:

Techniques used by the poet:

Activity 2

20 MINS

1 Look at the poems in the anthology collection that you have studied. Choose at least six devices that the poets have used to convey their ideas, attitudes, thoughts or feelings. The examples should come from at least two different poems.

2 Complete the table opposite. The first example (one from each collection) has been completed for you. Add extra rows if you have time.

Poem	Device/feature	Quotation	How this helps the poet to convey ideas, attitudes, thoughts or feelings
Relationships: *Valentine*	Metaphor	'It is a moon wrapped in brown paper'	The poet compares the onion (symbolising her love) to the moon, suggesting romance and mystery as well as light. The everyday words 'brown paper' contrast strongly with the more exciting image of the moon, suggesting that there is more to the lover than meets the eye.
Clashes and collisions: *Exposure*	Repetition	'But nothing happens'	Repeated at the end of the first, third, fourth and last stanzas, emphasising the repetitive nature of trench life and the futility of the war. The soldiers have sacrificed everything, but nothing has improved.
Somewhere, anywhere: *Orkney/ This Life*	Onomatopoeia	'When a clatter of white whoops and rises...'	The two words 'clatter' and 'whoops' give a vivid impression of the noise made by the rising sea-bird mentioned in the previous stanza. This continues the image of the couple's relationship being closely linked to their environment.
Taking a stand: *Solitude*	Contrast	'Feast, and your halls are crowded;/ Fast and the world goes by'	The contrast of 'feast' and 'fast', with similar sounds but opposite meanings, is an effective way of showing the huge difference between the two lifestyles which the poet describes.

Poem	Device/feature	Quotation	How this helps the poet to convey ideas, attitudes, thoughts or feelings

Activity 3

20 MINS

In this activity you are going to practise planning a response to a sample examination question.

1 Read the question relating to the collection of poems you have studied. Then read the poem. Try and look at a copy of the poem that you have not previously annotated to practise the skills you will need in the examination.

Relationships

Explore how the writer conveys his thoughts and feelings about his dead wife in 'My Last Duchess'.   (15 marks)

Clashes and collisions

Explore how the writer conveys his attitudes towards the conditions experienced by the soldiers in 'Exposure'.   (15 marks)

Somewhere, anywhere

Explore how the writer's conveys his attitude towards Romney Marsh in 'In Romney Marsh'.   (15 marks)

Taking a stand

Explore how the writer communicates his thoughts and feelings about global warming and climate change in 'One World Down the Drain'.   (15 marks)

2 The first stage of your plan is to think about the key points you want to make in response to the question. Write down three key points you will argue in the table opposite.

3 For each point you make, you must include evidence from the poem. To get the best marks, you must choose really good examples to convince the reader that your point is sound. Write down **one or two** examples from the poem that you will use to support your point. In the examination, you may wish to use more examples, if appropriate.

4 Now write a brief explanation of how the examples you have given support your point. You may need to continue your response on a separate piece of paper.

Point	Evidence	Explanation
The narrator shows that he was displeased and jealous that the Duchess did not give him the respect he felt he deserved compared with other men.	'She thanked men– good! but thanked Somehow–I know not how–as if she ranked My gift of a nine-hundred-years-old name With anybody's gift.'	The writer's choice of words shows that he did not expect her to show the same gratitude to others as she did to him, because his 'gift' of an ancient family name should have been seen as far better and the only thing she should have been grateful for.
He has a strong sense that the weather is as much of an enemy as are the Germans	'The poignant misery of dawn begins to grow…' 'We only know war lasts, rain soaks, and clouds sag stormy.'	The writer uses metaphor and personification to show the new day as being an enemy, with the bad weather coming to attack the soldiers.
The writer shows how strongly he was affected by the sights he saw on his walk.	'I saw the yellow sunlight fall On knolls where Norman churches stand.'	The writer's choice of words shows his appreciation of the effect of the light falling on the ancient Churches – the word 'Norman' shows that these have stood for up to a thousand years.
He shows that he believes that the beautiful city of Venice will be destroyed by global warming, and that people do not care enough to prevent its destruction.	'Book flights to Venice now. It won't be there in fifty years – Great City. Pity. Ciao.'	The writer here gives the idea that the threat of destruction is so great that if people want to see Venice they need to go quickly. The line 'Great city. Pity. Ciao' Is effective, because it shows how casual people are about the loss of such a great city.

10 MINS

1 Look closely at the extract below from a student answer to the question on your chosen collection that you planned a response to in Activity 3.

Ask yourself:

- Has the student made an interesting, relevant point?
- Have they given evidence from the poem to support their point?
- Have they explained how the evidence supports their point?

2 Use the Higher Tier mark scheme opposite to decide which band you think the answer would achieve.

Relationships

The Duke saw his wife as a possession, with her portrait seen only when he wishes ('none puts by the curtain I have drawn for you but I'). This reveals powerfully the Duke's feelings about her. His pride was wounded by her open nature: 'she liked whate'er she looked on, and her looks went everywhere.' The Duke's broken speech ('-all and each would draw from her alike the approving speech, or blush') shows his disgust at her lack of respect for him; she had 'much the same smile' for anyone. The dramatic monologue form reveals the Duchess's looks and actions but also the Duke's interpretation of her nature.

Clashes and collisions

Wilfred Owen conveys strongly how the forces of nature seem to be against the soldiers in the line; 'We only know war lasts, rain soaks, and clouds sag stormy.' The juxtaposition of the short, sharp words 'War lasts' and 'Rain soaks' shows that incessant rainfall is unavoidable in the trenches. As rain soaks through your clothes, the relentlessness of war permeates the spirit. The last phrase brings the ideas together: the stormy rainclouds link in the soldier's mind to the clouds of smoke from gunfire or the threatening gas clouds.

Somewhere, anywhere

The poem has striking images of Romney Marsh at day and night, creating snapshots of this memorable area. It moves from the isolated Norman churches recalled in the 'yellow sunlight' to the veil of 'purple vapour' and the sapphire air. The images create a mystical and magical landscape: the reader sees the changes of light transform the landscape. There is a constant appeal to the senses: sounds are emphasised in the evocative phrases 'swinging waves pealed;' and 'diamond drops/And beads of surge prolonged the roar'. The writer brings out the majesty of the Marsh at different times of day. The last stanza effectively mirrors the fourth, focusing on the sea and shore. At the end, the waves 'clashed on the shore' in the darkness but the 'pealing' sound, with the metaphor of the 'organ stops' and the assonantal 'o' in 'prolonged the roar', shows the never-ending sound of the sea.

Simon Rae's bitter satire attacks the short-sighted views of the planet he meets. His vivid images of the destruction of the planet bring home the catastrophe he fears. He sees Venice sinking beneath the water as a terrible tragedy, in a powerfully staccato line, using internal rhyme and one-word sentences: 'Great City. Pity. Ciao.' This angry, dismissive tone is because he fears that people's obsession with living only for the present will stop action to end global warming, as he shows again in the final epigram: '(The future has no vote)'. His ironic tone of voice underlines how politicians appeal to voters with immediate rewards, not considering what will happen in fifty years.

Band	Description
3	• Thorough explanation of how the writer conveys his attitudes to create effect • Sustained, relevant connection made between attitudes and the presentation of ideas • Sustained, relevant textual reference to support response
4	• Assured explanation of how the writer conveys attitudes to create effect • Relevant connection made between attitudes and the presentation of ideas • Pertinent textual reference to support response
5	• Perceptive explanation of how the writer uses attitudes to create effect • Discriminating, relevant connection made between attitudes and the presentation of ideas • Convincing, relevant textual reference to support response

ResultsPlus
Build your skills

Fill in the RAG table below to see how your confidence has improved in the following areas:

	R	A	G
I can recognise a range of poetic devices and comment on their effect	○	○	○
I can comment on the effect of particular vocabulary	○	○	○
I can comment on the effect of the structure and form of a poem	○	○	○
I can choose relevant examples from the poem to support my points	○	○	○

3 Comparing two poems

I need to:
- make comparisons and links between the poems
- compare the ways the two poets present their ideas
- use relevant quotations to support my ideas.

This lesson will help you prepare for the Section B Anthology Poems section of your examination. This lesson focuses on **part (b)** of the examination question. This will ask you to compare the way two writers present their ideas about the same theme.

You should answer **either** part (b)(i) **or** part (b)(ii).

- **Part (b)(i)** will ask you to compare the writer's ideas in the poem from part (a) with another named poem from the anthology collection you have studied.

- **Part (b)(ii)** will ask you to compare the writer's ideas in the poem from part (a) with a poem of your choice from the anthology collection you have studied.

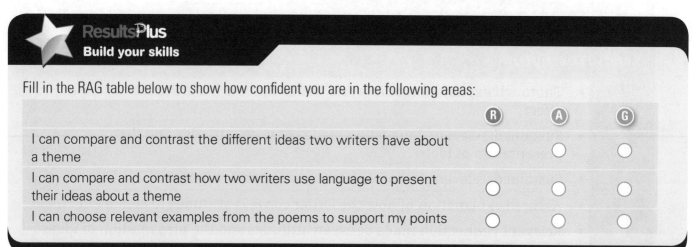

ResultsPlus
Build your skills

Fill in the RAG table below to show how confident you are in the following areas:

	R	A	G
I can compare and contrast the different ideas two writers have about a theme	○	○	○
I can compare and contrast how two writers use language to present their ideas about a theme	○	○	○
I can choose relevant examples from the poems to support my points	○	○	○

Activity 1

10 MINS

In part (b) of the examination, you will need to compare how writers present their thoughts, feelings, ideas or attitudes. Before you go into the examination, it is important to have a good understanding of the main themes, ideas and feelings in the poems you have studied.

1 Look at the ten words in the table opposite which describe feelings. Choose five of these and note down one of the poems in your collection which presents each of them.

2 Now write down other words to describe the feelings in each of the five poems.

3 Write down a word with an opposite meaning to the original key words. Find five poems in your collection that present these opposite feelings. Note down other words to describe the feelings presented in the poems.

Key words to describe people's feelings	Poem which has this feeling	Other words to describe feelings and attitudes in poem	Word with opposite meaning	Poem with this feeling	Other words to describe feelings and attitudes in poem
bitter					
frustrated					
tender					
disappointed					
excited					
passionate					
loving					
irritated					
affectionate					
hostile					

Activity 2

When you are looking at two poems, you are looking for things that are similar in the writers' ideas or approach, as well as things that are different.

1   Look at the poems specified below for your collection. Without referring to your notes, write down what you think is the main theme/idea in each poem and the techniques used by the writer.

Relationships

'Sonnet 116' and 'One Flesh'

Clashes and collisions

'The Drum' and 'O What is that Sound'

Somewhere, anywhere

'Cape Town morning' and 'Composed upon Westminster Bridge, September 3 1802'

Taking a stand

'Zero Hour' and 'One World Down the Drain'

Poem 1

Main theme/idea

_____

_____

The feelings/attitudes expressed in the poem

_____

_____

Writer's techniques

_____

_____

Poem 2

Main theme/idea

The feelings/attitudes expressed in the poem

Writer's techniques

2   Now write a paragraph to briefly explain to what extent the two poems are
    similar or different. Are the ideas, thoughts and feeling expressed similar,
    different or partly similar and partly different? Are the techniques they use
    similar or different?

Activity 3

20 MINS

In this activity you will practise planning an answer to a part (b)(ii) question. In your answer, you should include points of comparison, include pieces of evidence, and explain how this evidence supports your comparison.

1 Look at the question relating to the anthology collection you have been studying. One of the poems has been chosen for you.

Relationships

Compare how the writers of 'The Habit of Light' and one poem of your choice reflect on family memories. (15 marks)

Clashes and collisions

Compare how the writers of 'Your Dad Did What?' and one poem of your choice reflect on misunderstandings that can occur between people. (15 marks)

Somewhere, anywhere

Compare how the writers of 'City Jungle' and one poem of your choice reflect on a place. (15 marks)

Taking a stand

Compare how the writers of 'Pessimism for Beginners' and one poem of your choice reflect on people's perceptions of each other. (15 marks)

2 Choose a suitable poem to compare with the one named in the question. Think carefully before choosing a poem: you can choose a poem that presents similar ideas or different ideas but you do need to be able to make useful comparisons between the two. Don't just pick a poem at random!

Chosen poem: _____

_____

Unsuitable poems: _____

_____

3 Now you need to think about the key comparisons you want to make in response to the question. Write the key comparisons in the table below.

Point (comparison)	Evidence (Poem 1)	Evidence (Poem 2)	Explanation

4 For each comparison you make, you must include evidence from both poems. Add examples to the table from each poem that you will use to support your point. In the examination, you may wish to use more examples, if appropriate.

5 Write a brief explanation in the table of how the examples you have given support your comparison.

10 MINS

1 Look at the Higher Tier mark scheme. To write the best answer you can, it is important to know what you are aiming to do. Rewrite the following criteria for Band 5 of the mark scheme in your own words. You may find it helpful to use a dictionary.

Band	Description
3	• Specific and detailed comparisons and links • Developed evaluation of the different ways of expressing meaning and achieving effects • Selection of examples is detailed, appropriate and supports the points being made
4	• Assured comparisons and links • Pertinent evaluation of the different ways of expressing meaning and achieving effects • Selection of examples is assured, appropriate and supports the points being made
5	• Discriminating comparisons and links showing insight • Perceptive evaluation of the different ways of expressing meaning and achieving effects • Selection of examples is discriminating; fully supports the points being made

a **Discriminating** comparisons and links, showing **insight** into the poem.

I need to _____

_____

_____

b **Perceptive** evaluation of the different ways that writers express their ideas and achieve effects.

I need to _____

_____

_____

c Selection of examples is **discriminating**; fully supports the points made.

I need to _____

_____

_____

2 Look again at the planning you did in Activity 3. Do you need to make any improvements to your points, evidence or explanation? Explain any changes you would like to make.

_____

_____

_____

_____

3 Write at least one paragraph in answer to the sample examination question in Activity 3, using your revised plan. Always aim for the top band!

_____

_____

_____

_____

_____

_____

_____

_____

ResultsPlus
Build your skills

Fill in the RAG table below to see how your confidence has improved in the following areas:

	R	A	G
I can compare and contrast the different ideas two writers have about a theme	○	○	○
I can compare and contrast how two writers use language to present their ideas about a theme	○	○	○
I can choose relevant examples from the poems to support my points	○	○	○

Published by Pearson Education Limited, Edinburgh Gate, Harlow, Essex, CM20 2JE.

www.pearsonschoolsandfecolleges.co.uk

Text © Pearson Education Limited 2012
Designed and typeset by Juice Creative Limited, Hertfordshire
Cover illustration by Miriam Sturdee

The rights of Janet Beauman, David Grant, Alan Pearce, Racheal Smith and Pam Taylor to be identified as authors of this work have been asserted by them in accordance with the Copyright, Designs and Patents Act 1988.

First published 2012

16 15 14
10 9 8 7 6 5 4 3

British Library Cataloguing in Publication Data
A catalogue record for this book is available from the British Library.

ISBN 978 1 446904 39 8

Printed in Slovakia by Neografia

Acknowledgements
Extracts on pages 8, 16, 24, 32, 96, 104 from *Of Mice and Men* by John Steinbeck, Penguin, 2000, copyright © 1937 by John Steinbeck, renewed © 1965 by John Steinbeck. Reproduced by permission of Penguin Books Ltd and Viking Penguin, a division of Penguin Group (USA) Inc.; Extracts on pages 9, 17, 25, 32, 97, 105 from *To Kill a Mockingbird* by Harper Lee, published by William Heinemann, copyright © 1960 by Harper Lee, renewed © 1988 by Harper Lee. Reproduced by permission of The Random House Group Limited, Aitken Alexander Associates and HarperCollins Publishers; Extracts on pages 72, 74, 78-9, 80, 82, 86, 88 from *Animal Farm* by George Orwell, copyright © 1945 by George Orwell, copyright © 1949 by Harcourt, Inc. and renewed 1977 by Sonia Orwell. Reproduced by permission of Bill Hamilton as the Literary Executor of the Estate of the Late Sonia Brownell Orwell, Secker & Warburg Ltd and Houghton Mifflin Harcourt Publishing Company. All rights reserved; Poetry on pages 122-123 from 'In Mrs Tilscher's Class' by Carol Ann Duffy, from *The Other Country* published by Anvil Press Poetry © Carol Ann Duffy, 1990. Reproduced by permission of Anvil Press Poetry and the author c/o Rogers, Coleridge & White Ltd., 20 Powis Mews, London W11 1JN; Poetry on page 124 from 'The Warm and the Cold' by Ted Hughes, Faber and Faber Ltd, copyright © Carol Hughes, Estate of Ted Hughes; Poetry on page 124 from 'I am the wind', copyright © Dr Silvia Hartmann, www.1-poem.com; Poetry on page 124 from

'The City' by Langston Hughes, from *Collected Poems of Langston Hughes*, Alfred A Knopf/Vintage, copyright © 1994 by the Estate of Langston Hughes. Reproduced by permission of David Higham Associates and Alfred A. Knopf, a division of Random House, Inc.; Poetry on page 132 from 'Valentine' by Carol Ann Duffy, from *Mean Time*, 1993, copyright © Carol Ann Duffy, 1990. Reproduced by permission of Anvil Press Poetry and the author c/o Rogers, Coleridge & White Ltd., 20 Powis Mews, London W11 1JN; Poetry on page 132 from 'Orkney/This Life' by Andrew Greig, from *This Life, This Life: Selected Poems 1970–2006*. Published by Bloodaxe Books, 2006; Poetry on page 135 from 'One World Down the Drain' by Simon Rae, from *Earth Shattering: Ecopoems* by Astley, N., Bloodaxe Books, 2007, copyright © Simon Rae. Reproduced with permission of the author.

Every effort has been made to contact copyright holders of material reproduced in this book. Any omissions will be rectified in subsequent printings if notice is given to the publishers.

In order to ensure that this resource offers high-quality support for the associated Edexcel qualification, it has been through a review process by the awarding organisation to confirm that it fully covers the teaching and learning content of the specification or part of a specification at which it is aimed, and demonstrates an appropriate balance between the development of subject skills, knowledge and understanding, in addition to preparation for assessment.

While the publishers have made every attempt to ensure that advice on the qualification and its assessment is accurate, the official specification and associated assessment guidance materials are the only authoritative source of information and should always be referred to for definitive guidance.

No material from an endorsed revision workbook will be used verbatim in any assessment set by Edexcel.

Endorsement of a revision workbook does not mean that the revision workbook is required to achieve this Edexcel qualification, nor does it mean that it is the only suitable material available to support the qualification, and any resource lists produced by the awarding organisation shall include this and other appropriate resources.